# DEVON BUTTERFLIES

### C . R . BRISTOW   S . H . MITCHELL
### D . E . BOLTON

**DEVON BOOKS**

First published in Great Britain by Devon Books, 1993.

Authors addresses:
C.R. Bristow, Davidsland, Brendon Hill, Copplestone, Devon EX17 5NX
S.H. Mitchell, 26 Mellons Close, Newton Abbot, Devon TQ12 1YF
D.E. Bolton, Royal Albert Memorial Museum, Queen Street, Exeter EX 4 3RX

Cover photograph. Large Blue, female, Hartland 1971 (T. Jenkyn).

ISBN 0 86114 884 3

Publishing and Sales:
Devon Books, 1 Chinon Court, Lower Moor Way, Tiverton EX16 6SS. (0884) 243242

Printed by BPCC Wheatons Ltd, Exeter, Devon, UK.

Sponsored by:
    British Gas PLC (South Western).
    Butterfly Conservation.
    The Devonshire Association.
    Watts Blake Bearne & Co PLC.
    Claude & Margaret Pike Woodlands Trust.

BUTTERFLY
CONSERVATION

# CONTENTS

# List of figures

# List of plates

# Species List

## Pieridae

## Lycaenidae

## Nymphalidae

| n | White Admiral | 12a | 90 |
|---|---|---|---|
| n | Purple Emperor | | 94 |
| c+ | Red Admiral | 12b | 95 |
| c+ | Painted Lady | 12c | 96 |
| r | Scarce Painted Lady | . | 97 |
| n | Small Tortoiseshell | 12e | 99 |
| ?e | Large Tortoiseshell | 12f | 99 |
| r | Camberwell Beauty | | 101 |
| n | Peacock | 12d | 102 |
| n | Comma | 15b | 103 |
| n | Pearl-bordered Fritillary | 13a, 13b | 106 |
| n | Small Pearl-bordered Fritillary | 13c, 13d | 107 |
| r | Queen of Spain Fritillary | 15a | 108 |
| a | Aphrodite Fritillary | | 109 |
| n | High Brown Fritillary | 14a, 14b | 109 |
| n | Dark Green Fritillary | 14c, 14d | 112 |
| n | Silver-washed Fritillary | 14e, 14f | 112 |
| n | Marsh Fritillary | 13e, 13f | 114 |
| * | Glanville Fritillary | | 119 |
| n | Heath Fritillary | 15c | 119 |

## Satyridae

| n | Speckled Wood | 15d | 125 |
|---|---|---|---|
| n | Wall | 15e | 126 |
| a | Scotch Argus | | 126 |
| n | Marbled White | 15f | 127 |
| n | Grayling | 16a | 128 |
| n | Gatekeeper | 16b | 130 |
| n | Meadow Brown | 16c | 131 |
| n | Ringlet | 16d | 132 |
| n | Small Heath | 16e | 133 |
| ? | Pearly Heath | | 134 |

## Danaidae

| r | Monarch | 16f | 134 |
|---|---|---|---|

a  accidental; c  common immigrant; d  deliberate introduction
e  extinct; n  native; r  rare immigrant ; * record in error;
?  status uncertain; +  immigrant, sometimes breeding.

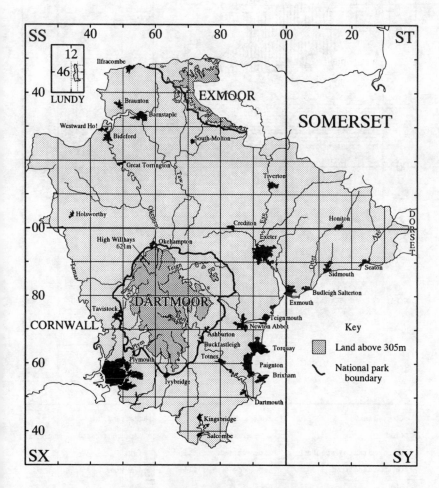

Figure 1: General topography of Devon.

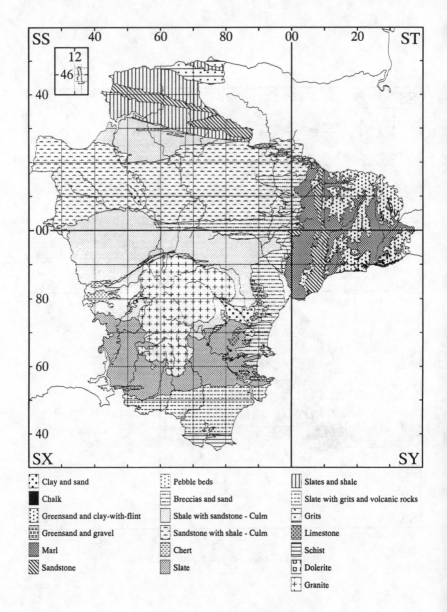

Figure 2: Geology of Devon (simplified).

# 1. INTRODUCTION

Devon is the third largest county in England, with an area of 6,711km$^2$, nearly 3% of the land area of Britain. Within the county, the altitude ranges from sea level to 621m (2038ft, Figure 1), geological formations vary from acid granite to alkaline limestone, and from free-draining sandstone to heavy clay (Figure 2). Rainfall varies from 800 to 2,000mm annually (Figure 3), and is directly related to the position of the high ground. The mean January temperature varies from 5 to 7C°, and mean July temperature from 17 to 18C°. Thus, Devon encompasses a wide variety of habitats. Excluding the rough grazing on Dartmoor and Exmoor, farming accounts for 5,200km$^2$ (77%) of the land surface (Waldron in Sitters, 1988).

With such variety, it is not surprising that Devon supports a large number of butterfly species - forty-three regularly breed in the county. At the turn of the century, the number was forty-nine. What is surprising, is that with such a number, Devon has never been regarded as an important butterfly county nor regularly 'worked'. A few lists of butterflies have been published (Reading, 1862; Parfitt, 1878; Barrett, 1906 and Stidston, 1952), but they are not comprehensive, particularly with regard to distributions. In autumn 1984, the Devon Butterfly Mapping Scheme was launched in an endeavour to determine accurately the distribution of Devon's butterflies. In particular, so that informed decisions could be taken to protect them and their habitats. The tetrad[1] was decided as a convenient mapping unit for the county. This was in line with atlases for the flora (Ivimey-Cook, 1984) and breeding birds (Sitters, 1988). There are 1834 in Devon. By the end of 1991, 380 recorders had contributed 69,000 records. The distribution maps are a direct result of that work.

## Geology

The tourist thinks of Devon as a county of granitic tors and red soils. In fact, both occupy a relatively small area of Devon (Figure 2). Broadly, Devonian and older deposits lie south of Dartmoor, and north of Barnstaple, with Carboniferous deposits in between. Permian and Triassic deposits occur primarily east of Exeter.

The southern Devonian outcrops are dominantly of shale and slate that break down slowly to give heavy clay soils. Much of the land is Grade 3 or 4[2] and intensively farmed. Slates are interbedded with lenticular bodies of limestone in the Torquay, Brixham, Buckfastleigh and Plymouth areas. Limestone

1 Tetrad: A 2 by 2km square bounded by the even numbered grid lines.
2 Agricultural land classification: Land with moderate (3), severe (4) or very severe (5) limitations due to adverse soil characteristics, and adverse relief or climate. Land above 1000 feet is Grade 5.

1

and chalk-based soils are particularly important, being uncommon, and a pre-requisite for lime-loving plants and the butterflies that depend on them.

The Devonian rocks of western Exmoor consist of an interbedded sequence of slates and sandstones. Small lenticular beds of limestone, up to 17m thick, occur in the middle of the sequence. Soils developed on these strata are thin and acidic; those over the slates are commonly peaty gleyed podzols. Whilst marginal areas have been reclaimed, most of the moor is given over to rough grazing.

The Culm measures are dominantly clayey sediments of Carboniferous age; they occur over half of the county, principally in west and mid-Devon. The sediments give rise to heavy, poorly drained clay soils (Grade 3, 4 or 5). Much of the land underlain by Culm is damp meadows, which until 'improved' are important species-rich habitats (Plate 5a). Some Culm grassland has been turned into conifer plantations, and some of the better-drained ground brought into arable use.

At the close of Carboniferous times, great changes took place, the most important for the present-day scenery was the intrusion of the Dartmoor granite. The granite, with its impressive tors, dominates the central southern part of Devon. It is an upstanding area of bare rock and acidic, peaty, and commonly boggy soils. Much of Dartmoor is open moorland used for rough grazing; some marginal areas have been reclaimed, and there are extensive conifer forests.

Following the intrusion of the granite, there was an extended period in which the 'New Red Sandstone' was laid down. It is these reddened sediments, comprising coarse breccias, conglomerates, sandstones and mudstones, so well exposed along the coast between Torquay and Dorset, that give the impression of Devon being a county of red soils. For the most part, the soils are fertile and, being a mixture of sand and clay, give rise to high-grade agricultural land (Grades 1 and 2). In East Devon, important heaths and commons have developed on the more arenaceous beds, and the pebble beds.

The red-bed formations are succeeded by a thick sequence of calcareous mudstones with thin limestone beds; these crop out on the valley sides north-east of Axminster and at the top of the cliffs east of Seaton. Geologically, a long break occurred between the deposition of these marls and the succeeding strata of Cretaceous age.

The Cretaceous deposits comprise the greensand hills of the Haldons and Blackdown, and the Chalk of East Devon. Much of the Chalk is covered by clay-with-flints which gives rise to acid soils. As with the Devonian limestones, the Chalk is important for its calcicole flora on which certain butterflies (Adonis and Chalk-hill blues) are dependant. Unfortunately, they no longer breed there.

# Rainfall

Altitude plays an important part in determining Devon's rainfall. As can be seen from Figure 3, the highest annual rainfall of 2000mm is over Dartmoor.

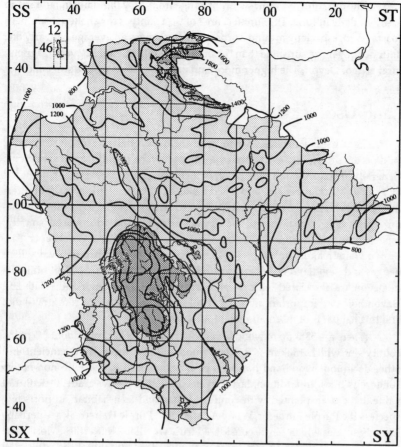

Figure 3: Average annual rainfall (mm) for 1941-1970.

Rainfall diminishes to half this figure along a line from the Torridge to the Exe estuaries, with the East Devon cliffs receiving less than 800mm annually. Rain does not fall evenly throughout the year. Average figures for the period 1961-1990 from North Wyke just north of Dartmoor, show a low in July (53mm), rising to a maximum in January (129mm); over 100mm falls in each month October to January.

## Temperature

The mean January temperature ranges from under 5C° in inland eastern parts of Devon, to over 6C° along parts of the southern and northern coasts. The mean July temperature lies in the range 16-17C°. These values decline by 0.6° for every 100m rise above sea level.

The duration of bright sunshine range from 1.5-2.0hr daily in January, to 6.5-7.5hr daily in June. The sunniest area of the county is the sheltered southern coastal strip, especially around Torbay, which receives an average of nearly one hour per day more sunshine than the bulk of the inland, more elevated, agricultural area of Devon. The higher moorland area receives even less sunshine.

# Land Use

Land use is a mix of arable and pasture in the rough ratio of 1:2. The arable land occurs principally in the drier eastern part of the county on red sandstone. Generally, fields are small and, except in rocky areas such as Dartmoor, bounded by hedges. Most arable and improved pasture fields are sterile areas for butterflies. However, field margins and hedgerows are extremely important habitats for a great many species, both for larval foodplants and adult nectar sources, especially for the commoner species such as the Ringlet and Gatekeeper. The Brown Hairstreak is an important Devon species, widespread in areas where hedges and woodland edges are rich in blackthorn (Plate 2a). Marsh Fritillaries in Devon are associated with rough pasture and grazed moorland (Plate 2b). Devon holds an important number of colonies, especially on Culm grassland, and this habitat is of international importance.

There are 538km$^2$ of woodland greater than 0.25 hectare - about 8% of the county - of which 160km$^2$ is ancient woodland. However, much ancient and other deciduous woodland has been clear felled and planted with non-native coniferous trees. In addition, large areas considered of low-grade agricultural value, have been planted with conifers. Woodland as a habitat supports few species - the Purple Emperor, White Admiral and Purple Hairstreak are perhaps the only species which can be considered truly woodland butterflies. Most of the other butterflies which we associate with woodlands (many of the fritillaries, Brimstone, Wood White etc.) are in fact species of woodland rides, glades (Plate 3b), and coppiced areas. If these open areas become overgrown, then the butterflies disappear. This is one reason why 'coniferisation' can initially have a beneficial effect on butterfly populations (Jenkyn, 1968). Some colonies of Heath Fritillary have thrived for a few years in plantain-rich meadows that have been planted with conifers. But as the conifers grow, they shade out other vegetation, and colonies rapidly decline. If however large open rides are permanently maintained, giving a woodland-edge type habitat, then many species can survive to breed. A particularly successful example is the colonisation of this habitat by the Wood White on Haldon Hills.

The heathlands of the East Devon commons are dominated by Gorse, various heathers, Heath Bent-grass and Purple Moor-grass and form a very important habitat (Plate 5b). The heath-loving butterflies such as the Small Heath and Grayling abound, together with lesser numbers of Green Hairstreak; some of Devon's most important colonies of the Silver-studded Blue occur on these commons. Four, and until recently six, of the seven Devon fritillaries breed here.

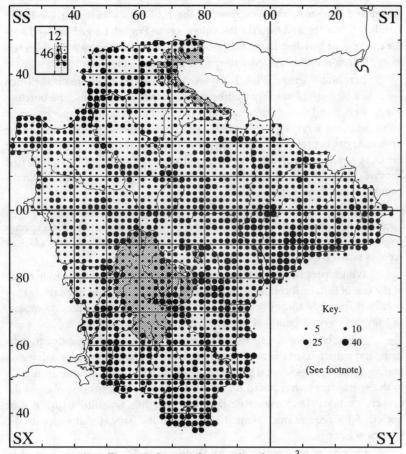

Figure 4: Species density distribution[3].

Venn Ottery Common, with forty butterfly species (this includes vagrants such as the Chalk-hill Blue), has the highest species count per tetrad in Devon. The value of these commons cannot be rated too highly, and the continuing threats to their survival must be strongly resisted.

The moorlands of Dartmoor and Exmoor are some of the wildest areas in Devon. Most of the moorland is used either as rough pasture or left uncultivated. Peripheral land is used as pasture (Plate 2b). Of the species associated with the moors, the Small Heath is probably the most ubiquitous. However, the wooded valleys (Plate 3a) draining the moor hold significant populations of

3. Spot area is directly proportional to the number of species recorded on that tetrad. They are continuously graded from 1 to 40 (40≡dia. 2Km). Example spots are given in the key. Records are taken from the following maps, and the maximum number of species is 39.

Green and Brown hairstreaks, most of the fritillaries - including the Heath Fritillary (Plate 1b), and held the last colony of the English Large Blue (and now the introduced Swedish Large Blue). Despite their wildness, new roads, reservoirs and reforestation are still eating in to these unspoilt areas.

Braunton Burrows (Plate 1a), which is built up from calcareous shell-rich sand, is a mixture of variably stabilised and mobile sand dunes. The burrows support a rich and varied flora, and this is reflected in the butterfly species which occur there: the Grayling is abundant; Dark Green Fritillaries are common; the Brown Argus is probably commoner here than anywhere else in Devon; both the Dingy and Grizzled skippers are plentiful, and the Small Blue, which first became evident in the latter part of the 1980s, probably has its best colony in the county on Braunton Burrows.

An indication of the distribution of butterflies and recorders is shown by Figure 4. Any tetrad below about 1000 feet ought to have at least ten species resident, if there are not, as in north and west Devon, then this reflects a lack of records rather than a lack of butterflies.

Whilst 'progress' has not been so severe in Devon as it has been in much of the rest of Britain, it continues to threaten many of the above habitats. Do not hold back from pointing out valuable sites that you know before they disappear, or sites that have deteriorated but which could be restored (Plate 4b).

Public bodies and private companies are increasingly sensitive to criticism, and conscious of the need for management of land they own. Advice on management regimes is often gratefully received. Many sites become unsuitable to the species they were noted for either due to the "hands off" policy of the conserving body/land owner or through changing agricultural practice or neglect. Sites require management to preserve the habitat that supports the species of interest.

Devon County Council, Devon Highways and local councils have all, in the past or currently, managed sites specifically for the benefit of wildlife. To take one example from the private domain: the Forestry Commission have established a Butterfly Walk in their Haldon forest (Plate 4a). This is an important site and much work has gone into creating and maintaining it in a suitable state.

For those of you for whom this book is the first introduction to Devon's butterflies, we hope that besides giving pleasure, it will stimulate you to a greater awareness of the dangers facing butterflies in the last decade of the twentieth century. Positive ways in which you can help are by joining the Devon Wildlife Trust, becoming a member (both nationally and locally) of Butterfly Conservation, and by contributing records to the Biological Record Centre at the Royal Albert Memorial Museum. By participating in the recording scheme, you will help us to monitor changes in the butterfly populations.

# History of recording

## Mainland Devon

Petiver, writing in the early eighteenth century, is reputed to have received several species from the county in material sent to him by Madam Glanville (of Glanville Fritillary fame) of Exeter (Emmet and Heath, 1989), but there is no species in his published work (Petiver, 1702-1706, 1717) that is recorded specifically from Devon.

Polewhele (1797) referred to a 'curious Black and White Butterfly in the woods at Lindridge' - this description can only be the Marbled White, although the possibility that it was the White Admiral cannot be excluded and leads to interesting speculation about its possible occurrence in the county two centuries ago.

Jermyn (1827) mentioned the Small Blue on Dartmoor, and the Chequered Skipper near Dartmouth.

In an undated work (post-1829 and thought to be 1830), Turton and Kingston produced one of the first lists of Devon butterflies, being a record of the species occurring in the Teignmouth, Dawlish and Torquay areas. It is an interesting list of seventeen species - most common butterflies (Large and Small White, Meadow Brown etc.) are missing, but several scarce (by today's standards) species (Heath Fritillary, Small Blue) are included. The complete list is Brimstone, Clouded Yellow, Orange Tip, Wood White, The Heath [Fritillary], Silver-washed Fritillary, Camberwell Beauty, Large Tortoiseshell, Painted Lady, Marbled White, Purple Hairstreak, Brown Hairstreak, Azure [Holly] Blue, Bedford [Small] Blue, Black-spot Brown [Silver-studded Blue], Mallow [Grizzled] Skipper and Dingy Skipper.

Fairweather (1844), in *Salcombe and its Neighbourhood,* has the earliest reference to the Large Blue in Devon, with occurrences between Bolt Head and Bolt Tail, and at Ashburton.

During the late 1850s and subsequently, there were many notes and short articles on the lepidoptera of Devon in the leading journals of the day. These included short lists at Martinhoe near Lynmouth (Horton 1857), Shaugh Common and Bickleigh Vale (Dell 1858), near Dawlish (Rawlinson 1858) and Exeter (Talpa 1859). An important list was by Mathew (1858c; 1860) entitled *List of Insects taken at Barnstaple etc., 1858*. Thirty-three species are mentioned, including all seven of Devon's fritillaries.

Many of the records from the above-mentioned articles were incorporated in Reading's (1862) list of the Lepidoptera of Devon and Cornwall. Fifty-two species of butterflies are listed, together with the reputed possibilities of two others (Comma and Glanville Fritillary).

Jordan (1874), in his natural history of Teignmouth and vicinity, listed 28 species, including the Large Tortoiseshell, all the fritillaries except the Marsh Fritillary, Large Blue (at Kingsbridge), and Small Blue.

Thirty-four species were listed by Nicholls (in Fox, 1874) for the Kingsbridge area. These included the Wood White, Large Tortoiseshell, Marsh Fritillary and Large Blue.

The next major county list was by Parfitt (1878) - fifty-four species (excluding varieties such as the *helice* form of the Clouded Yellow) are included. The additions to Reading's list being the Comma and the possible occurrence of the Aphrodite Fritillary.

Longstaff (1902, with additions in 1903 and 1904) produced a list of the lepidoptera of the Parish of Mortehoe. These were consolidated into his 1907b paper - forty species of butterflies are mentioned.

Barrett wrote the account of the Lepidoptera in the Victoria County History of Devon (1906); fifty-three species of butterfly are mentioned, of which the Sooty Copper caught near Ilfracombe in 1887, was included, but the Comma was omitted.

Lupton (1911), in an account of the flora and fauna of the Torquay district (defined as bounded by the sea, estuaries of the Teign and Dart, and the railway line from Newton Abbot to Totnes), added the Chalk-hill Blue (1899) and White-letter Hairstreak (1907) to the Devon list.

Walker (1930) reviewed the Macro-lepidoptera of the Torquay district (within a radius of about 20 miles of Torquay). Although the Long-tailed Blue had previously been recorded in Devon (see text), this was the first time that it was included in a local list (based on several specimens seen in September 1926). The record of three specimens of the Small Blue (in about 1926 according to Stidston (1952)) is of interest.

In *The Butterflies and Moths of the Neighbourhood of Exeter* (Solly, 1932), a loose geographical area that included Stoke Woods, Haldon, Dawlish Warren, Stover, Woodbury, and Ladram Bay, only seventeen butterflies are mentioned (common species such as the whites, Meadow Brown, Peacock etc. are omitted).

Thirty-four species were recorded by Wright (1932) within the Poor Law District of Braunton. There were no new species in the list, but it did include all Devon's fritillaries - except the Heath, together with the Silver-studded Blue.

In *The Fauna and Flora of Ilfracombe* (Palmer, 1946), forty-four species of butterflies were recorded. 'Ilfracombe' comprised a roughly ten-mile radius of that town and also included Lundy Island. Data from both Longstaff (1907b) and Wright (1932) were incorporated. One new species, the Scarce Swallowtail, that was captured at Woolacombe in 1901, and all seven of Devon's fritillaries, are included in this list.

John Heath, whilst stationed at Plymouth during the Second World War, compiled a list of the butterflies and moths of Devon. Although the section on the butterflies was written by F.W. Jeffery (of which, thanks to Paul Jeffery, we have an original annotated copy), the final typescript, of which there are several copies, came out under Heath's name (1946). We also have John Heath's annotated copy of the latter list. Fifty-seven butterflies are included; manuscript additions of the Swallowtail and the Black-veined White, brings the list up to fifty-nine. Species not previously recorded include the Scarce Painted Lady, White Admiral and Essex Skipper. Unlike previous compilations, the lists of localities are fairly extensive, particularly with the manuscript annotations, and there had been a good literature search, especially evident for the scarce migrants.

The best known, and most widely available account of the butterflies and moths of Devon prior to the Provisional Atlases, is Stidston's (1952) *A List of the Lepidoptera of Devon* published by the Devonshire Association. To a large extent, this was based on Heath's (1946) account, but it did contain much additional information. Sixty-three species were recorded, with one new name, the Scotch Argus, added to the county faunal list. This presumably was a misidentification, or an accidental introduction.

In the New Naturalist Series on Dartmoor (Harvey and St Leger-Gordon, 1953), the forty-five butterflies listed for Dartmoor appear to have been abstracted from Stidston (1952).

Two unpublished lists of local importance were produced by T.J. Wallace. The first, in 1967, dealt with the butterflies of the the Axmouth - Lyme Regis undercliffs National Nature Reserve. Thirty-eight species, including a Monarch in 1957, are recorded. The second list (1979), dealt with twenty-three of the scarcer species of East Devon.

The most recent list of local butterflies is for the Braunton Burrows (Harding, 1986).

## Lundy

The first record of the butterflies and moths of Lundy was by Chanter (1877) who listed twenty-one butterflies. Among the more surprising records, and for which there is no subsequent confirmation, are the Pearl-bordered, Small Pearl-bordered and Heath fritillaries. The inclusion of the Large Tortoiseshell was, for that time, not surprising. The record of the Comma is interesting as this would be one of the earliest records of that species in Devon (unfortunately the year of sighting was not given).

The Large Skipper was amongst six butterflies mentioned by Henderson (1885) on Lundy Island. It has not been recorded since, although it is interesting to note that the Small Skipper was recorded for the first time in 1989 (M.S. Warren). In July 1886, Henderson (1886) caught two Wall butterflies, a species not seen again for 100 years.

The only addition that Longstaff (1907b) made to the list of butterflies was the Grayling; surprisingly no Gatekeeper was seen.

The list of butterflies that appears in Loyd (1925) is taken from Heaven (1877).

Hart and Gray (1947) recorded thirteen common species, and Garrett-Jones (1969) saw nine of the above species in July 1968. Neither author saw a Peacock.

Dymond (1973) recorded fifteen species in 1972. These included the Gatekeeper, the first time since 1877, and the Holly Blue for the very first time (several specimens). In 1973, only one Holly Blue was seen, and no Gatekeeper. The above lists were incorporated in Sherwood (1975), but the Gatekeeper from the 1972 list was omitted. Gatekeepers were seen again July 18th 1989 (M.S. Warren).

Additional species seen up to the present day include the Wall (Aug. 11th 1986), Speckled Wood (Aug. 11th to Sept. 29th 1986), Green Hairstreak (June 22nd 1983, A.J. Parsons), Small Skipper (July 18th 1989, M.S. Warren), and after a gap of at least 50 years, the Brown Argus (July 27th 1989, A.M. Jewels).

A surprising omission from all but Heaven's (1877) list is the Orange Tip.

# Biographies

**ADAMS**, B.G. Collected in the Witheridge area 1904-1914. Material in the HEC.

**BARRETT**, Charles Golding (1836-1904). A Devon man by birth, Barrett's main contribution to the butterfly knowledge of the county is his account of the Lepidoptera published posthumously (1906) in the Victoria County History of Devon.

**BARTON**, I.B. (?-1986). Retired as a solicitor in Wimborne, Dorset, to Hartgrove House, near Trinity Common in East Devon, in 1970. He left his collection of butterflies and moths from around the house, to the Devonshire Association.

**BATTERSBY**, Robert (1786-1863). Battersby was one of the founder members of the Torquay Natural History Society in 1844, and its President in 1861, in which year he left Torquay to live in Ireland. He is of particular interest as having been born in the eighteenth century, although there are no butterfly records of his from that time. He contributed to Reading's (1862) *Catalogue of the Lepidoptera of Devon and Cornwall*. Amongst rarities seen or captured by him at Torquay were the Large Tortoiseshell, Heath and Marsh fritillaries, Adonis Blue, Lulworth Skipper and Camberwell Beauty (Battersby, 1859; Bracken, 1940a).

**BIGNELL**, George Carter (1826-1910). Born at Exeter on March 1st 1826, and educated at St John's College there. He joined the Royal Marines at Stonehouse in 1842. In 1862 he was discharged with the rank of Barrack-Master-Sergeant and with a Long Service Medal. He was appointed Registrar of Births, Deaths and Marriages, Poor Law Officer and Vaccination Officer for the Stonehouse District. From 1864, he contributed articles to *The Entomologist*, *Young Naturalist*, and was on the editorial staff of *The British Naturalist*. In 1893, he was elected President of the Plymouth Institution and Devon and Cornwall Natural History Society. He was a general naturalist with a special interest in entomology. He was awarded a Bronze Medal by the Royal Cornwall Polytechnic Society for a paper on Land and Freshwater shells. He died at Saltash. His entomological collection was presented by him to the then Municipal Museum at Plymouth in November 1909 (Morley, 1910).

**BRADEN**, B.P. (?-?1985). Braden kept a more or less continuous diary, in 15 numbered exercise books, from June 26th 1946 to Dec. 13th 1984 (now in the RAMM). He lived in North Somerset until about October 1972 and then moved to Tiverton, where he lived until his death in ?1985. In his diaries, he chiefly recorded the weather, flowers, birds and butterflies, but his interests in the different groups varied during the period of the diaries.

**BRODIE**, N.S. Brodie's collection of *c.*30,000 world lepidoptera was presented to the HEC in 1933 (Smith, 1986). It included material from Combe Martin (1896), Bolt Head - Large Blue (1890) and Sidmouth - Lulworth Skipper (1893).

**DIXEY**, Frederick Augustus (1855-1935). Collected with G.B. Longstaff in the Braunton Burrows and Mortehoe area in 1892. Material donated in 1897 to the HEC, with which he was associated from 1893 onwards. In the archives of the University Museum are two notebooks on Mortehoe lepidoptera 1879-1900 (Smith, 1986).

**GAY**, A.B. (1896-1959). Gay was a man of independent means. He purchased collections, cabinets and books for the RAMM; and arranged and classified all the foreign butterflies in the Consolidated Collection. In 1948 he joined the Devonshire Association, later serving on the Council, and was Vice Chairman of the Entomological Section. He was also a member of the Lundy Field Society Committee. For a while he lived at Lowerfield, Lapford, and later at Haldon House, Dunchideock.

**HAMM**, Albert Harry (1861-1951). A printer by trade, Hamm joined the Hope Department, Oxford, as an assistant in 1897, and continued there until his retirement in 1931 (Smith, 1986). He collected in the Newton Abbot, Bovey Tracey, Holne and Dawlish areas in 1898-1900. His material is in the Hope Collections.

**HEATH**, John (1922-1987). During the Second World War, he was stationed with the REME in Devon. He left Devon in 1946 to join the Biological Research Department of Pest Control near Cambridge. In 1953, he joined the Nature Conservancy, and in 1967 transferred to the newly formed Biological Records Centre at Monks Wood Experimental Station, with responsibility for setting up an insect distribution map scheme. The first of these was the *Provisional Atlas of Butterflies* in 1970 which provided the impetus for so many local mapping schemes. Whilst stationed in Devon, with the help of F.W. Jeffery, he compiled a list of Devon butterflies and moths (1946), but the list was never published. However, the list was passed to S.T. Stidston and incorporated, with minimum acknowledgement, in Stidston (1952). Both John Heath and F.W. Jeffery gave us copies of their own annotated lists.

**HELLINS**, Revd John (1829-1887). Some time after his ordination, he became second master at Exeter Grammar School, and in 1859, he succeeded his father as Chaplain to the Devon County Prison. He later became curate at St

11

Petrock's, Exeter. Bracken (1940a) recorded that he kept diaries continuously from 1851 to 1887, the present whereabouts of which is unknown. He was particularly successful in rearing lepidopterous larvae, and is best known for his collaboration from 1858 -1884 with William Buckler in the production of *The Larvae of the British Butterflies and Moths*. Various notes of Hellins (sometimes under the name of 'Talpa') are to be found in the entomological journals of the day, including the Victoria County History list of Barrett (1906) (Bracken, 1940a).

**HOLCROFT**, C.W. (*c*.1893-1976). On his retirement as a solicitor, just before the Second World War, he moved from Birmingham (where he had collected butterflies as a schoolboy) to Lustleigh, Devon. He collected butterflies mainly in the Lustleigh, Bishopsteignton (where he later lived) and Hennock reservoir areas. His collection, diaries (1953-5, 1963, 1966) and books were presented to the RAMM by his widow in 1976.

**JEFFERY**, Frederick William (1903-1974). A schoolmaster for many years, he retired as deputy headmaster of Burleigh Secondary School, Plymouth. He was a longtime member of the Plymouth and District Field Club, serving as their President from 1940-1943. He was a member of the Devonshire Association from 1938 until his death, and founder member of the Entomological Section. He was a Council Member from 1968-1971, Vice-President in 1974, and Chairman of the Plymouth Branch in the same year. His collection was housed in the Plymouth Athenaeum, but in 1990 it was given to the Devon Branch of Butterfly Conservation.

**JORDAN**, William Risdon Hall (1821-1911). Hall was born, educated, worked and died in Teignmouth. His family had settled at Teignmouth in about 1650. He was admitted as a solicitor in 1844, subsequently serving in various local government offices in Teignmouth. He joined the Devonshire Association in 1871, and at one time was on the Council. He was also a member of the Teign Naturalists Field Club. He is perhaps best known for his paper on the *Natural History of Teignmouth and its Vicinity* (1874). In the HEC archives, there is Dale manuscript entitled *List of Lepidoptera in Museum Jordan, Teignmouth, March 1841*.

**LANG**, Revd H.C. Collected in the Ivybridge area in 1889. Possibly he supplied R. Meldola with material from this area. His collection passed, via Rowland-Brown, to the HEC in 1914 (Smith, 1896).

**LEES**, Frank Henry (1883-1973). He was born in Birmingham where he lived for his first 55 years, and from which area he built up a fine collection of lepidoptera. He retired from his own brass foundry firm in 1935 and moved to Maidencombe, and proceeded to build up a substantial local collection. His collection of moths, especially those caught in Kent, included an amazing number of rarities. He was a founder member of the Entomological Section of the Devonshire Association. His Devon collection was purchased by the Association in 1967 and is housed in Exeter University.

**LONGSTAFF**, George Blundell (1849-1921). Longstaff is best known in Devon for his list of insects from the Mortehoe district (1902; 1903; 1904;1907b)

12

and from Lundy (1907a). He also published several accounts of foreign butterflies; one of his best-known works is *Butterfly Hunting in Many Lands* published in 1912. Material from the Mortehoe district is in the HEC, Oxford.

**MATHEW**, Gervase Frederick (1842-1928). Mathew lived at Raleigh House near Barnstaple until he joined the Royal Navy as a clerk in 1861. As a teenager, he contributed several papers on the butterflies and moths of the Barnstaple area. He was stationed at Dartmouth for a while and continued to publish notes on the butterflies of that area. He travelled extensively in service, and studied the lepidoptera of the Mediterranean region as well as parts of the Pacific Zone. In 1886, he was posted to H.M.S. Penelope at Harwich, Essex, subsequently becoming District Paymaster to the Harwich Coastguard. He retired from the Navy in 1902, moved to Lee House, Dovercourt, where he remained until his death. In Essex, he continued to study and write about the local lepidoptera, his last paper being published in 1925.

**PALMER**, Mervyn Grove (1882-1954). From 1904 until about 1931, Palmer spent much of his life in South and Central America where he collected a great variety of zoological specimens. A collection of foreign butterflies is in the Ilfracombe Museum; some of his material is in the British Museum (Natural History). On his return to England, he settled at Ilfracombe where he was instrumental in setting up the Ilfracombe Field Club (in 1933), and founding the Ilfracombe Museum. He was a Fellow of the Royal Geographical Society and the Royal Entomological Society, and a Member of the British Ornithological Union. He also acted as President of the South-Western Naturalists Union. Judging from the specimens in his collection in the Ilfracombe Museum, he appears to have done only a limited amount of butterfly collecting in the Ilfracombe area. However, he is best remembered for compiling the list of butterflies and moths for *The Fauna and Flora of the Ilfracombe District* (1946), of which book he was also the editor.

**PARFITT**, Edward (1820-1893). Parfitt was born in Norwich in 1820, but moved early in life to Hereford where his father was head gardener to the Dean. After a trip to South Africa, he came to Devon where he continued gardening, later becoming Curator of the Taunton Museum. In 1861, he was appointed Librarian of the Devon and Exeter Institution, a post which he held to his death. He was a prodigious writer on many aspects of natural history, including various groups of insects, archaeology, marine life, conchology, algae, botany, birds, reptiles and meteorology. Because of his wide-ranging interests, his work was not thorough and brought him much criticism (Bracken, 1940a). After his death, his large collection of insects was lost sight of for many years. However, in 1932, they were presented to the Torquay Natural History Society, but unfortunately they were destroyed by museum beetles by 1952, and no record of its contents were kept (Heckford, 1984, p. 60).

**READING**, John Joseph. A prominent member of the Plymouth Institution in the 1860s, being Curator of Entomology from 1861-1863. He was an artist of distinction, in particular of birds and insects. Reading left Plymouth in the

1870s. His collections passed to J. Brooking Rowe, who presented them to the Royal Albert Memorial Museum in January 1904. He is best remembered for his *Catalogue of the Lepidoptera of Devon and Cornwall* published in the *Transactions of the Plymouth Institution*, of which Part 1, the butterflies, appeared in 1862. He published many entomological notes, together with *Notes on the rarer birds of Plymouth* in the *Zoologist*.

**SIDGWICK**, N.V. Collected in the Dartmouth area in 1896. Material from this area, together with his entomological diaries, passed to the HEC in 1929 (Smith, 1986).

**SPOONER**, G. Malcolm (1907-1989). Born at Yelverton, he was educated at Charterhouse and Christ's College, Cambridge, where he graduated with a first in zoology in 1929, and went that same year to work as a Student Probationer at the Plymouth laboratory of the Marine Biological Association, a post he retired from in 1972. He joined the Devonshire Association in 1948, was Honorary Editor from 1967-73, President in 1979, and became an Honorary Member in 1983. He was a recorder and Chairman of the Entomological Section for many years. He was also an active member of the Botanical section and participated in the recording for the *Atlas of the Devon Flora*. For fifteen years he served on the Dartmoor National Park Committee. He was a founder member of the Devon Wildlife Trust, Chairman of the Committee for the Conservation of the Large Blue, a Fellow of the Royal Entomological Society and a leading authority on British Hymenoptera. At the start of the Devon butterfly survey, Malcolm combed through his diaries and contributed a vast number of records.

**STIDSTON**, Stanley Thomas (1881-1963). Educated at Mutley Grammar School, Plymouth, from where he entered the Royal Naval Engineering College and rose to the rank of Captain. He served in both world wars. He joined the Devonshire Association in 1934, and became secretary of the Entomological Section when it was founded in 1948, until 1961. One of Stidston's notable finds, in company with J. Walker, was a colony of Large Blue on the southern slopes of Dartmoor in 1936; a second colony was found in 1948. Stidston is best known for his *List of the Lepidoptera of Devon, Part 1*, published by the Devonshire Association in 1952 (Part 2 was never published).

**STUDD**, Edward Fairfax (1855-1942). Eldest son of Major-General Edward Studd, J.P., D.L., of Oxton, formerly High Sheriff of Devon. Educated at University College, Oxford, obtaining his B.A. in 1878 and his B.C.L. in 1881. He became a student of the Inner Temple in 1878, and was called to the Bar in 1881. He was a magistrate for Devon. He lived at Inverness for a time, then at Oxton in the parish of Kenton, and later at Exeleigh, Starcross. Studd was a great sportsman and was for a time master of the Haldon hunt pack. However, Studd's great hobby throughout his life was the collection of British butterflies and moths, many of which he bred (the necessary foodplants were bought in by his gardeners every morning). He had three light traps in his woods, the paraffin lamps of which were trimmed and filled daily by one of his gardeners. Studd was elected a Fellow of the Entomological Society in 1895, and remained a member until 1919. After his death in 1942, his collections, diaries and books were presented to the RAMM by his widow.

**TALPA** - see HELLINS, Revd J.

**WALKER**, J. ( -1949). Walker was a prominent member of the Torquay Natural History Society from 1910 until his death. He published several articles on entomology in their journal, of which one of the most important was a review of the *Macrolepidoptera of the Torquay district* (1930). He found (with S.T. Stidston) a colony of the Large Blue on Dartmoor in 1936.

**WOODFORDE**, Francis Cardew ( -1928). Woodforde gained his MA at Exeter College, later becoming headmaster of Market Drayton Grammar School until his retirement in 1909. He moved to Oxford, and assisted Prof. Poulton with the arrangement of the collections of British lepidoptera. Material collected in 'N. Devon' and Paignton in 1913 is in the HEC.

**WATKINS**, O. George (1905-1991). He began his career as a teacher in Plymouth at Public Central School for Boys, and remained a teacher all his life. He was a founder member of the Devon Trust for Nature Conservation (now Devon Wildlife Trust), vice-chairman of the entomological section of the Devonshire Association, and an active member of the Plymouth and District Field Club. His interests were wide ranging, specialising in butterflies, birds, and fungi. He is well remembered as a breeder of butterflies, and for his almost life long interest in Andrews Wood.

**WRIGHT**, F.R. Elliston, FRES (1879-1966). A doctor by profession, he is best known for his book *Braunton. A few nature notes* (1932).

# Devon collections and diaries

B.G. Adams (HEC).

G.C. Bignell (Plymouth City Museum).

B.P. Braden (Diaries to RAMM, 1990).

N.S. Brodie (HEC, 1933).

J. Brooking Rowe (RAMM, 1904).

R.J. Champion (HEC, 1919).

C. Chichester (RAMM, 1938).

F.A. Dixey (HEC, 1897).

H.L. Earl (Torquay Natural History Society Museum, 1937).

N.P. Fenwick (RAMM, 1928).

Ford (RAMM, 1925).

A.B. Gay (RAMM, 1930-1959).

A.H. Hamm (HEC).

Headley Moore (Plymouth City Museum).

J. Hellins (RAMM, 1907, 1918).

C.W. Holcroft - Butterflies and diaries (RAMM, 1976).

F.W. Jeffery (Plymouth Athenaeum); the collection was given by the Athenaeum to the Devon Branch of Butterfly Conservation in 1990.

W.J. Kerr (Torquay Natural History Society Museum, 1937).

H.C. Lang (via Rowland-Brown to the HEC, 1914).

G.B. Longstaff (HEC).

H. Lupton (Torquay Natural History Society Museum, 1932).

E.D. Morgan (Torquay Natural History Society Museum, 1931).

M.G. Palmer. Collections of both foreign and British lepidoptera are in the Ilfracombe Museum; some foreign material is in the Natural History Museum, London.

E. Parfitt. His collection passed to the Torquay Natural History Society in 1932, but the collection had been destroyed by beetles by 1952 (Heckford, 1984).

J.J. Reading (RAMM, 1904, via J. Brooking Rowe).

F.R. Rowley (RAMM).

G.E. Shelley (HEC, 1922).

N.V. Sidgwick (Diaries and specimens in the HEC, 1929).

E.F. Studd - Books, diaries and collections (RAMM, 1913; 1942; 1943).

Warmsley-White - Diaries (RAMM).

F.C. Woodforde (HEC).


# Check-list of Devon butterflies

Some seventy-five butterfly species have been recorded or are reputed to have occurred in Devon during the last 160 years:

**Resident:** 42 species

| | |
|---|---|
| Small Skipper | Essex Skipper |
| Large Skipper | Dingy Skipper |
| Grizzled Skipper | Wood White |
| Brimstone | Large White |
| Small White | Green-veined White |

| | |
|---|---|
| Orange Tip | Green Hairstreak |
| Brown Hairstreak | Purple Hairstreak |
| White-letter Hairstreak | Small Copper |
| Small Blue | Silver-studded Blue |
| Brown Argus | Common Blue |
| Adonis Blue | Holly Blue |
| White Admiral | Purple Emperor |
| Small Tortoiseshell | Peacock |
| Comma | Small Pearl-bordered Fritillary |
| Pearl-bordered Fritillary | High Brown Fritillary |
| Dark Green Fritillary | Silver-washed Fritillary |
| Marsh Fritillary | Heath Fritillary |
| Speckled Wood | Wall |
| Marbled White | Grayling |
| Gatekeeper | Meadow Brown |
| Ringlet | Small Heath |

**Common immigrants which usually breed in the county:** 4 species

| | |
|---|---|
| Red Admiral | Painted Lady |
| Clouded Yellow | Large White - immigration commonly reinforces the native population |

**Re-established species:** 1 species

Large Blue

**Scarce immigrant species** 10 species

| | |
|---|---|
| Swallowtail | Scarce Swallowtail |
| Pale Clouded Yellow | Berger's Clouded Yellow |
| Bath White | Long-tailed Blue |
| Scarce Painted Lady | Camberwell Beauty |
| Queen of Spain Fritillary | ?Aphrodite Fritillary |

**Extinct species:** 8 species

| | |
|---|---|
| Chequered Skipper (?1870s) | Lulworth Skipper (?1920s) |
| Silver-spotted Skipper (?1910s) | Chalk-hill Blue (1981) |
| Large Blue (1979) | Black-veined White (1850s) |
| Duke of Burgundy (1940s) | ?Large Tortoiseshell (1950s) |

**Accidental introductions:** 5 species

| | |
|---|---|
| Fiery Skipper | Southern Festoon |
| Sooty Copper | Green-underside Blue |
| Scotch Argus | |

**Former status (if ever) uncertain:** 3 species

| | |
|---|---|
| Large Copper | Middle Copper |
| Pearly Heath | |

**Species included in error:** 4 species

| | |
|---|---|
| Black Hairstreak | Purple-shot Copper |
| Short-tailed Blue | Glanville Fritillary |

# Acknowledgements:

Many people and organisations have contributed towards the compilation of this book. In addition to all those who took part in the recording scheme (listed separately below), the following, in alphabetical order, deserve special mention:

The Biological Records Centre, Monks Wood, have provided us with distribution data on the scarcer Devon butterflies; John Breeds lent us the Braunton Burrows habitat shot (Plate 1a); the late Russell F. Bretherton helped with information on the scarcer immigrants; Butterfly Conservation (Devon Branch) (formerly British Butterfly Conservation Society) for allowing us to photograph and reproduce (Plates 8d, 10c, 12f, 15a) material in the Jeffery Collection; David Carter of the Natural History Museum, London, for photographs of the Scarce Swallowtail (Plate 7a) and the Green-underside Blue (Plate 10e); Mr B. Chatfield provided the photograph (Plate 9f) of the White-letter Hairstreak; the Devonshire Association has kindly allowed us to incorporate records from their manuscript butterfly 'book'; the Devon Wildlife Trust has provided us with data over the years from many of their reserves; Mr M. Dean helped us by tracking down an obscure reference; Exeter City Council for their support in setting up the Devon Biological Record Centre and for printing and photographic help; Dr E. C. Freshney wrote, and has continually modified as need arose, the computer programme for the butterfly recording scheme; Mr. R. Goodden has kindly supplied the slide of the Adonis Blue (Plate 11d); the late John Heath kindly supplied us with an annotated copy of his 1946 list of Devon butterflies; Paul Jeffery gave us an annotated copy of his father's 1946 list of Devon butterflies, manuscript notes and newspaper cuttings; Dave Jenks gave his time and expertise to help construct the maps; Tom Jenkyn went through his old diaries and provided us with a wealth of data for the period prior to the start of the butterfly recording scheme and he provided the cover photograph and plates 10d and 11f; many of the illustrations are from the collection of David, Hazel and Michael Land (see photographic credits); Mr I. Lansbury of the University Museum, Oxford, allowed us to examine the Hope Entomological Collections (including the Dale Collection) and has helped with bibliographical references; Mr S.E. Moore has diaries going back to 1919 and has kindly extracted relevant material from them; Denis Pickering lent us a habitat shot (Pate 3b); Mr C. Pratt has given us details of early records of the Comma in Devon; Tom Sleep has kindly read and commented on various sections of the text; Mrs J. Slocombe of the Ilfracombe Museum allowed us to examine the collections, and to photograph and reproduce one of the specimens therein (Plate 10b); David Smallshire has helped us with the text on the High Brown Fritillary and provided some of the habitat shots (Plates 3a and 5a); the late Malcolm Spooner waded through his diaries and produced a vast volume of data for the period prior to the start of the butterfly mapping scheme, together with help on sections of the script; Jeremy Thomas has provided invaluable help and criticism for the account of the Large Blue; Roger Thornett made important comments to improve parts of the account, especially Marsh Fritillary; Plate 16f is of a specimen in the collection of Mr V.R. Tucker; Ray Tye lent us several slides of the butterflies illustrated in the account (see photographic credits); Ken Tyson provided the meteorological data and notes which appear in the introductory chapter; Tom Wallace gave us copies of his typescript lists of East Devon butterflies; Martin Warren's help with the section on the Heath Fritillary is much appreciated; the late Mr O.G. Watkins supplied us with pre-1985 data from his diaries; Watts Blake Bearne & Co PLC for the use of their desktop publishing and photocopying equipment; the only record of Berger's Clouded Yellow was supplied by Mr D. Worton and who has kindly allowed us to photograph it (Plate 7d). The staff of the Entomological Library of the Natural History Museum, London, have been very helpful with bibliographical enquiries.

## Recorders 1985-93.

Without the help of the several hundred recorders listed below, it would not have been possible to produce the detailed distribution maps included throughout the text, nor to write with authority, several of the species accounts. We hope that no one has been omitted from the list, but if they have, they receive our sincere apologies. To all these people we are most grateful:

J. Ainsworth, J.Allen, P.F. Allfrey, R. Apsey, A. Archer-Lock, J. Armsworth, R. Arter-Williamson, H. Ayshford,

B.A. Baker, F.E. Baker, M. Baker, N.M. Baldock, J. Bannerman, J. Banning, S. Barlow, G.J. Barnes, S.L. Barnes, H.N. Barns, D. Barrett, J. Barrett, I. Barton, D.M. Basey, K. Bastow, E.T. Bayliss, P.J. Bedford, T. Beer, B. Benfield, D. Benfield, T. Bennett, T. Besterman, B. Blackmore, M. Blackmore, J. Bloomfield, R.W. Bogue, D.E. Bolton, E. Bond, J.M. Bond, I. Booker, K.J. Boot, J.E. Bottom, R.H. Bowden, J.C. Bowring, B.P. Braden, J. Braven, N.W. Briden, M. Bridget, F.E. Bridle, F.J. Briggs, C.R. Bristow, P.D. Bristow, H.J. Bristow, M.J. Bristow (Mr), M.J. Bristow (Mrs), S. Brown, S.D. Bruce, S. Buckthorpe, R. Bulcraig, K. Buller, A.N. Burgess, P. Burston, G. Burt, J. Busby, J. Butter, P. Butter, A. Breen,

J. Campbell, D. Capon, N.D. Capper, J.F. Capper, A. Catt, M. Catt, F. Challenger, Mrs Chandler, G.M. Chapman, P. Chapman, B. Chatfield, J. Cherrington, D.J. Churchill, R.J. Clarke, D.V. Clish, J.M. Clitherow, O.M. Comont, P. Coombs, J.M. Cook, K. Cook, P. Corbin, C. Courtenay, C. Craik, L.J. Craik, A. Croft, V. Croft, C. Cross, P. Crotty, R.F. Crouch, A.E. Crumby, B.M. Cummins,

J. Daniel, S. Dart, R.J. Darwen, I. Davies, M. Davis, S. Davis, K. Davis Monk, B.H. Dickens, J. Dignam, B.J. Douglass, E.W. Douglas, Mr Dowden, J. Downes, A. von Drieberg, P. Dukes, K. Duncan, M.R. Dunn,

A. Eastman, M.R. Edmonds, A. Edwards, B.V. Edwards, M. Edwards, S. Edwards, H.W. Eldridge, P. Ellacott, M. Elliott, D. Ellis, W.A. Ely, E. Endacott,

T. Farley, G. Fenton, F. Ferguson, M.H. Ferris, E. Field, J. Field, B.L. Finzel, G. Flower, S.J. Ford, G.F. Foster, G.F. Foster, R.G. Fowle, J.G. Fox, S.D. Foxhall, K.A. Franey, E. Franks, A. Fraser, E.C. Freshney, J.R. Freshney, N.H. Fresson,

J. Gapper, J. Garden, A.J. Gardiner, I.M. Gardiner, P. Gardner, W. Garforth, H. Garton, Mr Geary, D.A. Gee, M.C. George, J.G. Gill, M. Gillingwater, Mrs Gillot, K. Goatly, M.J. Goddard, P. Goddard, A.J.J. Goode, P.F. Goodfellow, Mr Goodman, K.A. Gosling, A.M. Gotham, P. Gotham, D.A. Gough, E.L. Grace, M. Gray, P.R. Green, R. Greenway, R. Greenwood, P. Greeves, 'Green Lanes', A.C. Griffith, P.M. Grogan, G.H. Gush, J. Guyers,

E.C.M. Haes, G. Haig, P.E. Haines, J.B. Hammond, B. Hardman, B. Harley, W. Harley, J. Harris, E. Hart, M. Hart, R.J. Hart, S. Hateley, A.R. Hawtin, R. Haynes, Mrs Hayward, M. Hazell, P.S. Head, J. Headon, R.J. Heckford, J. Heath, R. Heath, B.P. Henwood, J. Heywood, J. High, D.M. Hill, R.M. Hill, S. Hillier, D. Hinde, M. Hodges, W.J. Hodgetts, R.M.H. Hodgson, D. Hogge, J.R. Holden, A. Holmes, D.J. Hopkins, K.D. Hopwood, Mrs Hoskings, R.J. Hubble, M.R. Hughes, J. Hunt, H.G. Hurrell, L.H. Hurrell, J. Hustedt, S. Huxton,

G.J. Kacanow, B. Kail, D.M. Kemp, J. Kenderdine, G.E.C. Kenton, L. Kerry, R. Khan, H.T. King, J. Kingsley-Smith, O. Knight,

D.G.S. Lambert, D.J. Land, H. Land, M. Land, M. Lander, M. Lavelle, C.J. Lavington-Evans, R.M. Lawson, Mr Ledger, M.J. Lee, E.J. Lenton, J.D. Leslie, W.F.J. Leverton, M.I. Lewis, F. Ley, V. Ley, A. Liebert, K. Lilly, J.A. Lindley, R. Linter, M.B. Littans, L. Lock, B. Lockton, C. Longworth-Dames,

H. Macey, Q. & J. Macdonald, A.G. Mackonochie, S.G. Madge, C. Maguire, E. Mallinson, N. Malton, H. Marshall, N. Marshall, B. Martin, J.A. Martin, J. Masson, E.N. Masson-Phillips, J.L. Masson-Phillips, M. McKeever, R. McLindon, Mrs Meardon, C. Mellet, B.J. Melloy, M.A. Middleton, J. Millman, M.J. Mitchell, S.H. Mitchell, P. Michelmore, R.H. Montgomery, S.E. Moore, S.L. Moore, P. Morgan, P.H. Morris, M.J. Mugford, D. Munden, W. Murray, G. Musker, S.P. Mutlow,

R.H. Newland, J.A.S. Newman, P. Noakes, M. North, M.M. Nunn,

J. Oates, M. Oates, H.L. O'Heffernan, M. Oliver, M. Olver, K.J. Orpe, M. Orr, D. Overy, D.M. Oxtoby,

Lion Pack, I.D. Page, P. Page, W. Parkin, D. Parsley, C.R. Parsons, E. Parsons, B. Pateman, S. Payne, Q. Paynter, E.C. Pelham-Clinton, A.M.C. Penno, R.J. Perkins, A.B. Pettigrew, J. Pettyfer, M. Phillips, F.R. Philps, T.A. Pickard, D. Pickering, G. Pilkington, J. Pitman, F.J. Polkinghorne, M. Pool, D. Pope, E. Pope, G. Pope, M.A. Pope, S. Pope, M.J. Preston, A. Price, B. Price, B.P.R. Primmer, W. Putt, P. Quicke,

D.C.M. Radford, G. Ramsdale, D.J. Ramdsen, J. Randall, J.M. Randall, P. Reed, C. von Reibnitz, J. von Reibnitz, S. von Reibnitz, M.A. Reynolds, E. Richardson, I. Rippey, J. Robbins, J. Robertson, D.A. Rogers, J. Rooker, J. Roskell, P. Rosser, A.O. Rowden, J.F. Russell,

A.J. Saltern, P. Sanders, H.A. Sandford, E.A. Sarl, B. Saunders, H.J. Scott-Forbes, R.C. Scrivener, R. Seaward, G.D. Seccombe, D. Sharpe, W. Sharpe, J.M. Shaw, J. Shelston, C.H. Shere, M. Sherratt, P. Sherratt, V. Sherratt, J. Siewruk, M.E. Simmonds, S.P. Simmonds, Sixth Kingsbridge Cub Scouts, J.M. Sleep, T.D. Sleep, N. Smallbones, D. Smallshire, C.G.W. Smith, M.E.A. Smith, R. Smith, C.A.P. Smout, C. Soakes, A.J.R. Softly, B. Softly, K. Spalding, L.M. Spalton, K. Sparks, P. Sparks, G.M. Spooner, C. Steel, D. Stevens, M.L. Stevens, P. Stevens, J. Stock, P. Stone, R. Sutcliffe, D. Sutton, R.D. Sutton, J. Summerscales, I.D. Swatridge, C. Sweeney, Mrs Sweetman, J. Swinfen,

J. Tallowin, E. Tapp, P. Tapp, D. Taylor, J. Taylor, P. Tead, C.M. Thompson, J. Thorne, M.J. Thornett, R.C. Thornett, P. Tolley (Mr & Mrs), E. Towns, S. Toyn, S.M. Tracey, K. Tucker, N. Tucker, V.R. Tucker, W.H. Tucker, H. Turner, J. Turner, J.P. Turner, M.A. Turner, D.R. Tye, O.E. Tye, J.D.A. Tyers, H.M.K. Tyers, C. Tyler-Smith, K.C. Tyson,

N.K. Van der Kiste, R.E.G. Van der Kiste, G.A. Vaughan, N.J. Venn, G. Vernall, J. Vickers,

L. Wall, M. Wall, T.J. Wallace, R. Waller, N.W. Ward, M.S. Warren, G. Waterhouse, O.G. Watkins, P. Watkin-Williams, R. Weaving, C. Webb, D. Webb, P.A. Wedd, P.J. Weddell, K.A. Westcott, G. Weymouth, M.J. Wheatley, C. White, R. White, T. White, M. Willcocks, E. Williams, M. Williams, V. Williams, P.M. Williamson, J. Willis, R. Wills, A. Woodland, D. Woodland, J. & J. Woodland, H. Wooltorton, L. Wraith, R.D. Wren, M. Wright,

D.J. Yardley, M. Yelland.

**Sponsors.**

We would like to thank those individuals and companies who at the completion of this work gave us financial assistance. Without this timely help the production of this book would have been severely delayed.

British Gas PLC (South Western), Riverside, Temple Street, Keynsham, Bristol BS18 1EQ.

Butterfly Conservation, P.O. Box 222, Dedham, Colchester, Essex CO7 6EY.

The Devonshire Association For the Advancement of Science, Literature and the Arts, 7, Cathedral Close, Exeter EX5 4EY.

Watts Blake Bearne & Co PLC, Park House, Courtenay Park, Newton Abbot TQ12 4PS

Claude & Margaret Pike Woodlands Trust, Dunderdale Lawn, Penshurst Rd, Newton Abbot TQ12 1EN

# Abbreviations:

| | |
|---|---|
| BC | Butterfly Conservation |
| BM(NH) | British Museum (Natural History) |
| BRC | Biological Record Centre |
| Dev. Ass. | Devonshire Association |
| D&S | Denis & Schiffermüller |
| HEC | Hope Entomological Collections |
| L. | Linnaeus |
| NCC | Nature Conservancy Council |
| RAMM | Royal Albert Memorial Museum |
| Rott. | Rottemburg |

# Some Addresses:

Butterfly Conservation, P.O. Box 222, Dedham, Colchester, Essex CO7 6EY.

Butterfly Conservation (Devon Branch), Secretary, Mrs B. Jordan, Stable Cottage, Dunchideock, Exeter EX6 7YD.

Devon Wildlife Trust, 188 Sidwell Street, Exeter EX4 6RQ.

The Devonshire Association, 7 The Close, Exeter EX5 4EY.

Royal Albert Memorial Museum, Queen Street, Exeter EX4 3RX.

# Essential Notes:

## The Maps:

All records from the survey up to 1990 are included in the maps, along with selected additions up to the date of publication. Land above 1000 feet has been highlighted. Numbers in the left hand column of the key refer to the number of tetrads with that category of occurrence.

In the case of the maps of the commoner species, only the modern (1980 to date) records are plotted.

## The Text:

Localities given are those where the butterfly was seen by the recorder concerned. A minor amount of renaming has been done by us to give greater consistency of names. If the record was accompanied by a grid reference, this is given to the nearest one kilometre square. Records with no grid reference are treated in two ways: i) we have inferred the grid reference, and indicated this by italicising it in the text; ii) none is given, the reader is left to decide where the site is.

## The Plates:

The plates comprise shots of some Devon habitats, and individual butterflies taken in Devon.

# 2. SPECIES ACCOUNTS

# Hesperiidae

## Chequered Skipper *Carterocephalus palaemon* (Pallas)

The Chequered Skipper became extinct in England in 1976; its former status in Devon is uncertain. Jermyn (1827) recorded it 'near Dartmouth'; Bostock (1857) mentioned a butterfly on a heath on the Abbotsham road near Bideford, which, 'to his inexperienced eye', looked like the Chequered Skipper. Morris (1876) gave Dartmoor as one of its localities. The Woodbury Common specimen caught by J.C. Jumenaux on August 1953 (Stidston, 1956) must be erroneous.

## Small Skipper *Thymelicus sylvestris* (Poda)                    Plate 6a

This is a fairly common, widespread species that is almost certainly seriously under-recorded. It probably occurs wherever there are tracts of the larval grasses - Yorkshire Fog *Holcus lanatus*, Cat's-tail *Phleum pratense*, Creeping Soft Grass *Holcus mollis* and False-brome *Brachypodium sylvaticum*. The reason for it being under-recorded is probably a combination of its relatively short flight period, its diminutive size and lack of distinctive features.

It normally flies from the beginning of July until mid-August. The earliest and latest dates are May 27th 1990 (P. Morris) and Sept. 10th 1986 (R.J. Clarke; K. Tyson).

## Essex Skipper *Thymelicus lineola* (Ochsenheimer)

The first Devon record of the Essex Skipper was at Newton Abbot in 1943 (Locke, 1950). Three were seen at Wembury on July 18th 1945 (O.G. Watkins) and another at Newton Ferrers on August 15th 1945 (J. Heath) (Heath, 1946). Riley (1947) stated that *lineola* was now to be found in 'South Devon'. The above occurrences, together with a record for 1948, are presumably the basis of Stidston's (1950) statement that it occurred in the South Hams district. There was no further record until 1969 when A.P. Gainsford saw 'small numbers flying with *sylvestris*' at the Warren, Wembury, on July 28th. One was seen in 1981 on the Aylesbeare/Harpford Common (I.D. Bullock). Finally, the Essex Skipper was seen again at Wembury in 1991 by M. Catt.

There were possible sightings at Stoke Hartland on Aug. 5th 1975 (T. Jenkyn), and north-east of Plymtree [ST0704] on July 9th 1989 (E. Mallinson).

In view of the difficulty of distinguishing the Small and Essex skippers (look for the black tips to the underside of the antennae of the latter species), and the fact that the Small Skipper is itself under-recorded, it would not be surprising

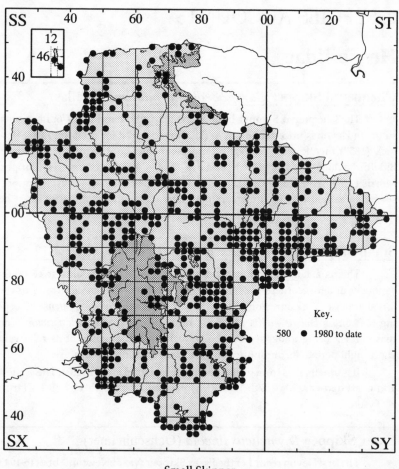

Key.

580 ● 1980 to date

Small Skipper

if the Essex Skipper turned out to be a resident in the county at several localities. Throughout much of south-eastern England, the two species often fly together.

---

## Lulworth Skipper *Thymelicus acteon* (Rottemburg)    Plate 6b

The stronghold of this species is Dorset. It bred in East Devon during the nineteenth and early part of the twentieth century, but despite occasional sightings, there is no evidence that it breeds in the county at the present day.

Stainton (1857), Norcombe (1857) and Gibbes (1858) have the earliest references to *acteon* in Devon - at Sidmouth. Reading (1862) described the Lulworth Skipper as extremely local in Devon - on the cliffs east of Sidmouth and at Torquay (on the authority of R. Battersby (Bracken, 1940a)). Parfitt (1878) found it on the grassy sloping cliffs beyond Exmouth, and east of Sidmouth. In August 1886, the colonies were 'more or less strong' (Perkins, 1936). In 1889, they were 'very abundant, but extremely local, I know of only one spot [near Sid-

24

mouth] where it occurs' (Majendie, 1891). In the HEC, there are five specimens from Sidmouth, caught July 20th 1893. In the Studd Collection (RAMM), there are eight Sidmouth specimens dated Aug. 4th 1897, and forty-seven specimens caught on July 19th 1899. Wells (1898) stated that *acteon* swarmed in its usual places [in South Devon]. Barrett (1906) added "Bere Regis" to the list of localities where the Lulworth Skipper could be found. Blathwayt (1909) recorded it '2 and a half miles west of Beer Head' in 1908, and in the same year, Whittle (1909) moaned that it took him 'two hours to get a dozen specimens', all males, mostly in only 'fair condition'.

In 1911 and 1913, Perkins (1936) recorded it at Sidmouth at the same places as in 1886. He implied that some colonies were still there 'not long after the war' [?1920], but noted that there were many collectors with 'big nets' working the area. He also stated that the Lulworth Skipper had not been seen in recent years and that it had 'certainly disappeared from several of the spots which it formerly frequented', but it is not clear whether he was referring to the 1920s, or to the time of his paper. Nevertheless, it is evident that some time between the 1920s and 1930s, the Lulworth Skipper in East Devon went into rapid decline and, except for a female caught by A.H. Dobson at the base of Sidmouth cliffs on Aug. 22nd 1967, it has not been seen since in East Devon. The occurrence of one on Berry Head on June 25th 1983 (C. & J. Johnson, K. Tucker and N.C. Ward) is a mystery, and a record from the South Hams coast in 1992 (M. Catt, *pers. commn.*) requires clarification.

Parfitt (1878) stated that it should be sought for in July and August, in the brightest and hottest weather.

## Silver-spotted Skipper *Hesperia comma* (Linnaeus)    Plate 6c

Little is known of the former distribution of this species, or when it became extinct, in Devon. Nationally, it used to be widely distributed on calcareous soils, particularly on the Chalk. In Devon, it was described as 'confined to the calcareous districts' (Barrett, 1906), although some of its quoted former localities (Exmouth) do not overlie calcareous soils.

Reading (1862) stated that he took one specimen in 1855 near Wembury, and that it was found along Embankment Road, Plymouth (R.B. Reed) and Exmouth (E. Parfitt) ['on the cliffs beyond' in Parfitt (1878)]. Harvie (1866) listed this species amongst his captures in South Devon in August 1866. Parfitt (1878) recorded that G.F. Mathew had taken one near Dartmouth. Majendie (1891) caught two specimens near Sidmouth in 1889. Barrett (1893) stated that 'Major Still has taken several this year on the slopes of Dartmoor'. In 1906, Barrett described *comma* as 'very local', and in addition to the above localities, added Sidmouth and Stoke. The last Devon record is an 'Exeter' specimen caught by E. Pope in 1907 (Plate 6c) and now in the Studd Colln., RAMM. The nearest extant colonies are in mid-Dorset.

## Fiery Skipper *Hylephila phyleus* (Drury)

Two specimens of this North American species were caught near Barnstaple by W. Raddon in about 1820. Shortly before their capture, a North American ship had unloaded its cargo of timber and other supplies, and is thought to have been the unwitting agent in the transport of the Fiery Skippers, either as adults or pupae (Emmet and Heath, 1989).

## Large Skipper *Ochlodes venata* (Bremer & Grey)         Plate 6d

This is a fairly widespread species that occurs throughout the county. It is the most widely recorded of all the Devon skippers. The larval foodplants include Cock's-foot *Dactylis glomerata* and False-brome *Brachypodium sylvaticum*.

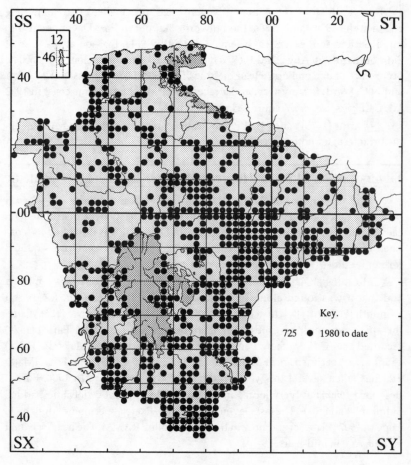

Large Skipper

The Large Skipper normally flies about a fortnight earlier than the Small Skipper, and can be seen from early June until mid-August. The earliest and latest dates are May 4th (Hinchcliff, 1893) and Sept. 7th 1985 (J. Garden).

## Dingy Skipper *Erynnis tages* (Linnaeus)                     Plate 6e

The Dingy Skipper is commonest along the cliffs of East Devon and at Braunton Burrows, with other small colonies scattered throughout the county. Unfortunately, the number and size of the colonies has declined over the last hundred years. The many earlier descriptions of it being common, unfortunately do not apply today: 'widely dispersed over the county' (Parfitt, 1878); 'common, sometimes abundant' in the Mortehoe district (Longstaff, 1907b); 'common' in the Ilfracombe area (Palmer, 1941); 'common around Newton Abbot' (Heath, 1946); 'plentiful and widely distributed' (Stidston, 1952).

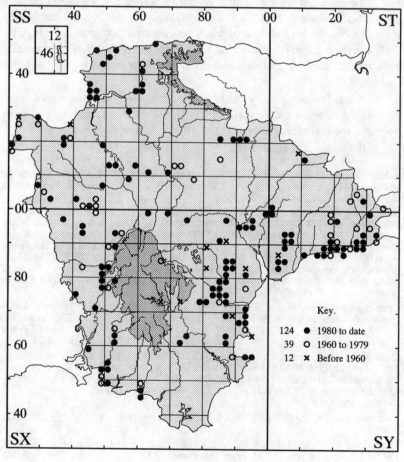

Dingy Skipper

Although usually single-brooded, in most years in Devon there is a partial second brood. The spring brood normally flies from mid-May (exceptionally mid-April - April 14th, 1893 (Hinchcliff, 1893)) until about mid-June (occasionally mid-July - July 19th, 1986, S.D. Bruce). The second brood appears at the end of July or early August (latest flying date, Sept. 6th 1987, T. Jenkyn).

The larval foodplant is Common Birdsfoot-trefoil *Lotus corniculatus*. Favoured plants for oviposition are associated with bare soil.

## Grizzled Skipper *Pyrgus malvae* (Linnaeus) Plate 6f

The Grizzled Skipper is an easily overlooked, small, elusive butterfly, although it has never been particularly common. The size of a colony can vary markedly from year to year. It used to be fairly widespread in Devon: 'not an abundant species, but it is widely dispersed' (Parfitt, 1878); 'not scarce' (Barrett, 1906); 'common and widely distributed' (Heath, 1946), 'common and generally distributed' (Stidston, 1952). Unfortunately, although still broadly distributed across the county, for the most part it is not common. Nationally, the marked decline in the number of colonies has been attributed to the effects of myxomatosis, modern farming methods and the reduction of coppicing (Emmet and Heath, 1989).

A small number of colonies have been discovered or rediscovered in the last five years. Some did exceptionally well in 1989; on Haldon, D. Pickering described them as more common than he had ever seen them before.

Below are set out all the Devon sites and latest record for the site:

**Ashclyst Forest** [SY0099], June 27th 1979, T. Jenkyn; May 18th 1986, D.J. Land. **Aylesbeare and Harpford Commons** *[SY0690]*, 1981, I.D. Bullock (Dev. Ass.). **Axmouth-Lyme Regis**, 1960; May 1966 (BRC, Monks Wood).

**Badgworthy Water, Malmsmead** [SS7945], June 18th 1986, M. & D. Blackmore. **Beadon Bridge, Hennock** [SX8181], June 1st 1970 (BRC, Monks Wood). **Beaworthy** *[SX4698]*, 1970, J.C.A. Craik (Dev. Ass.). **Bickington** [SX7972], 1992, a breeding colony, S.H. Mitchell. **Blackpool** [SX8173], 1992, a breeding colony, S.H. Mitchell. **Bovey Great Plantation** *[SX8275]*, 1961, A.H. Dobson (Dev. Ass.). **Bovey-Heathfield**, 1967, J.W.Phillips (Dev. Ass.). **Braunton Burrows**, breeding colony. **Bridestowe**, 1970, J.C.A. Craik (Dev. Ass.). **Brixham (Sharkham Point)** [SX9354], May 27th 1990, D. Hinde. **Bugford Valley, near Combe Martin** [SS6042], May 16th 1972, T. Beer.

**Chudleigh Knighton Heath** [SX8377], 1992, a breeding colony, S.H. Mitchell. **Churscombe, Paignton** [SX8762], 1991, L. Lock. **Clearbrook** *[SX5265]*, 1970, J.C.A. Craik (Dev. Ass.). **Paignton (Clennon Hill)** [SX8859], May 22nd 1952, B.P. Braden (Diaries). **Combe Martin**, June 1896 (HEC). **Culmstock Beacon** [ST1115], 1977 (BRC, Monks Wood).

**Dartmeet** *[SX6672]*, June 14th 1924 (RAMM). **Dawlish College, near Haldon** [SX9280], 1986; May 17th 1988, H. Wooltorton. **Dawlish Warren** *[SX9878]*, 1956, R.E. Melton (Dev. Ass.). **Double Waters, near Tavistock** *[SX4769]*, 1970, J.C.A. Craik (Dev. Ass.). **Dowlands Cliff** [SY2889], up to 1979 (Wallace, 1979). **Dunsford (Steps Bridge)** *[SX8088]*, 1950, A.H. Dobson (Dev. Ass.).

**Exeter (Beacon Heath)** [SX9495], 1965, R.J. Clarke. **Exeter (Exwick)** [SX9093], 1979, D.E. Bolton.

**Fernworthy dam** *[SX6784]*, 1970, J.C.A. Craik (Dev. Ass.). **Finlake, Chudleigh** [SX8479], 1992, a breeding colony, D. Smallshire. **Fordlands** *[SX8690]*, May 14th 1919 (RAMM). **Furley** [ST2604], May 9th 1948, T.J. Wallace.

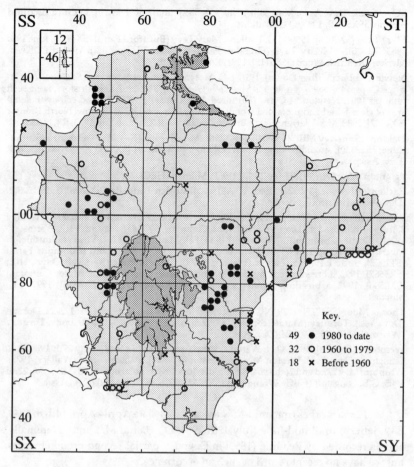

Grizzled Skipper

**Galmpton Quarry, Galmpton** [SX8856], June 5th 1965; June 5th 1988, C. Longworth-Dames. **Great Torrington** [SS5217], May 16th 1972, T. Jenkyn.

**Haldon,** 1992, a breeding colony. **Haldon (Buller Hill)** [SX8884], May 30th 1986, S. Buckthorpe. **Haldon (Harcombe Wood)** *[SX8882]*, 1963, A.H. Dobson (Dev. Ass.). **Halwill Junction** [SS4400], May 17th 1985, G.M. Spooner; June 14th 1986, A.W.G. John. **Halwill Moor Plantation** [SS4300], May 23rd 1977, T. Jenkyn. **Hartland Quay (St Catherine's Tor)** [SS2224], June 23rd 1947, E.C. Pelham-Clinton. **Hawkswood Reserve** *[SY2097]*, 1968; 1969; May 10th 1978, J.R.W. Coxhead (Dev. Ass.). **Heasley Mill (Long Wood)** [SS7533], June 16th 1986, M. & D. Blackmore. **Heddon's Mouth, Martinhoe** [SS6549], April 28th 1989, S.D. Bruce. **Hembury Wood (north)** [SS3720], June 2nd 1984, I.D. Page. **Hennock (Reservoirs)** *[SX8082]*, 1957, C.W. Holcroft (RAMM); June 24th 1985, S. Buckthorpe; May 25th 1986, D.J. Land. **Heybrook Bay** [SX4948], May 20th 1972, R.J. Heckford. **Highampton (Coombe Farm SSSI)** [SS4902], 1985; 1989, G.J. Barnes. **Hole** [SS4603], June 4th 1970, T. Jenkyn. **Holsworthy (Simpson Farm)** [SS3604], May 21st 1988, H. Marshall.

**Kenton (Oxton House)** *[SX9282]*, June 6th 1870; June 4th 1904 (Studd Colln.). **Kingswear,** 1924 (Dev. Ass.).

**Labrador Bay** *[SX9370]*, 1924 (Dev. Ass.). **Lapford,** May 31st and June 6th 1937, M.G. Palmer. **Liverton (near)** [SX8175], June 1st 1980 (BRC, Monks Wood). **Loddiswell** [SX7348], 1966 (BRC, Monks Wood). **Lydford (Coryhill Plantation)** [SX4783], April 23rd 1974, R.J. Heckford. **Lydford** [SX4882], 1972 (BRC, Plymouth). **Lydford (old railway)** [SX4983], 1970,

29

J.C.A. Craik (Dev. Ass.); May 28th 1990, T.D. Sleep and A.R. Hawtin. **Lydford (Lydford Station)** [SX5082], 1985, O.G. Watkins.

**Mary Tavy** [SX5078], 1980, O.G. Watkins. **Mary Tavy (Burnford Farm)** [SX4979], June 19th 1983, T.D. Sleep. **Mary Tavy (Grendon Farm)** [SX4876-78], June 12th 1988, T.D. Sleep. **Merton (Kennick Wood)** [SS5115], 1991, K.A. Westcott.

**Newton Abbot (Milber Down)**, 1910, E.D. Morgan (Dev. Ass.). **Newton St Cyres (Northridge Copse)** [SX8696], singletons May 26th 1986; May 31st 1987, C.R. Bristow; none seen June 1st 1991. **Newton St Cyres (Hundred Acre Copse)** [SX8596], good colony in small area of clear-felled and replanted woodland, May 17th 1992, C.R. Bristow. **North Brentor** [SX4982], 1983, M.S. Warren. **North Brentor (near)** [SX4679], June 15th 1973, R.J. Heckford.

**Oakford (Spurway Mill)** [SS8920], June 25th 1983, H. King (Dev. Ass.). **Oakford (Stuckeridge)** [SS9320], small breeding colony. **Okehampton (near)** [SX5493], 1970, J.C.A. Craik (Dev. Ass.).

**Paignton**, May 17th 1918; May 28th 1919, P. Milman (HEC).

**Rackenford Moor** [SS8521], 1983, P. Allfrey. **Rousden Landslip** *[SY2888]*, 1959, A.S.B. (Dev. Ass.); 1960 (BRC, Monks Wood).

**Saunton (Saunton Cliff top)** [SS4437], May 19th 1988, S.D. Bruce. **Seaton-Beer cliffs**, May 27th 1966, B.P. Braden (Diaries). **Shortwood Common** *[SY0583]*, May 8th 1917, Warmsley-White (Diaries). **Sidmouth (Peak Hill)** [SY1186], May 16th 1987, J. Vickers. **Southleigh (near)** [SY2091], up to 1979, B. Henwood (Wallace, 1979). **Stockland (Cummins Farm)** [ST2503], up to c.1979, S. Glover (Wallace, 1979). **Stoneycombe (Kerswell Down Hill)** [SX8667], 1992, a breeding colony, S.H. Mitchell. **Stoneycombe (Miltor Mator Common)** [SX8566], 1992, a breeding colony, S.H. Mitchell. **Stover Woods** [SX8375], 1991, S.H. Mitchell.

**Thorne Moor** [SS4115], 1979, NCC. **Torquay (Hope's Nose)** *[SX9463]*, 1951, A.H. Dobson (Dev. Ass.). **Torquay (Maidencombe)** [SX9268], May 3rd 1986, S. von Reibnitz. **Torquay (Watcombe)** *[SX9167]*, 1924 (Dev. Ass.).

**Wembury** [SX5248], 1964, O.G. Watkins. **Wembury Point** *[SX5048]*, May 27th 1969, A.P. Gainsford (Dev. Ass.). **Weston Mouth, Weston** [SY1688], 1973 and later (Wallace, 1979). **Whipton**, May 22nd and 26th 1964, B.P. Braden (diaries). **Woolacombe** *[SS4543]*, May 22nd 1905, G.B. Longstaff (HEC). **Wrangaton** *[SX6757]*, 1938, H.G. Hurrell (Dev. Ass.).

*P. malvae* flies from mid-May (occasionally late April - April 14th in 1948, F.W. Jeffery) until mid-June (July 13th 1986, D., H. and M. Land). Nationally, and as recorded by Reading (1862) in Devon, a partial second brood emerges, but we have no recent record of such an occurrence.

The larvae feed on a variety of plants including Barren and Wild Strawberry *Potentilla sterilis* and *Fragaria vesca*, Creeping Cinquefoil *P. repens*, Bramble *Rubus fruticosus* and Agrimony *Agrimonia eupatoria*.

# Papilionidae

## Southern Festoon *Zerynthia polyxena* ([D&S])

An example of this southern and central European species was caught by two boys on May 27th 1884 near Exeter (Parfitt, 1884). It was thought to be an imago reared from pupae imported by a dealer.

## Swallowtail *Papilio machaon* Linnaeus

Tutt (1895, p. 15) asked 'Can Mr Dobree Fox tell us anything about Devonian *Papilio machaon*? I know they are captured to the number of three or four nearly every year. Has the ground been salted and the insects now endeavouring to hold their own, or is it a dwindled down natural locality?' No reply was published to this intriguing question. Allan (1980) suggested that these reputed Devon occurrences were based largely on wishful thinking.

Below are set out all the Devon occurrences of the Swallowtail. They all probably belong to the continental subspecies *gorganus* Fruhstorfer:

1919 (or earlier), **Woodbury Common**, W.S. Lambshead (Accession Register, RAMM).

1934, **Torquay**, June 10th, S.E. Moore.

1943, **Sidmouth**, Aug. 10th, R.G. Sherlock (Sherlock, 1943).

1943, **'Cockington'**, July, larvae on "Milk Parsley" 'by one of the lakes', A.H. Dobson (Dev. Ass.).

1943, **Torquay**, Dr Gough (Dev. Ass.).

1950, **'Devon'**, September (Dannreuther, 1951, p. 102).

1959, **Sidmouth**, July, flying across the beach (Hunt, 1960, p. 14).

1964, **Bolt Head, Salcombe**, July 22nd, R.H. Clarke (Turner, 1965).

1976, **Slapton Ley Field Study Centre**, at a mercury vapour light (communicated to C.R. Bristow).

1984, **Slapton**, Aug. 30th, G.& J. Harrison.

1985, **Buckfastleigh**, Aug. 13th, J.A. Lindley.

1985, **Sidbury**, Sept. 26th, B. Softly.

[NB, Milk Parsley *Peucedanum palustre* has not been recorded as a wild plant, or escape, in Devon. However, two of the most widely used foodplants in Brittany are Fennel *Foeniculum vulgare* and Rock Samphire *Crithmum maritimum*; both plants are common on the south coast of Devon.]

## Scarce Swallowtail *Iphiclides podalirius* (Linnaeus)   Plate 7a

A small specimen was captured by H.E. Tracey at Willand in May 1895 (Heslop, 1958). A second occurrence, in 1901, was recorded by Frohawk in 'The Field' for July 6th 1935 from Woolacombe (Palmer, 1946, p. 73). This specimen is in the Natural History Museum collection - see plate.

# Pieridae

## Wood White *Leptidea sinapis* (Linnaeus)   Plate 7b

The distribution of the Wood White became very restricted early in the twentieth century, being found only in Devon, and the Hereford and Monmouth areas (Ford, 1945b), but it is not known whether there was also a decline within these counties. From 1926 to 1946, it became more widespread throughout the country.

From the available records, it is not possible to establish a definite picture of the status of the Wood White within Devon over the last 130 years. Even its current status is uncertain (see below). In the latter part of the nineteenth century, it was widespread and locally abundant, as can be seen from the following accounts :

According to Reading (1862), the Wood White was to be found at Plym Bridge, Shaugh Bridge, Berry Pomeroy, Torquay, Exeter, Axminster, Chudleigh and Buckfastleigh. In 1870, it was extremely abundant during late May and early June near Ipplepen - 'It does not appear to be confined to any particular locality, or to its usual resort of woods, being generally distributed, and occurring in almost every lane and hedge-row in this neighbourhood' (Wilkinson, 1870). 'The species is scattered, but not abundantly, all over the county' (Parfitt, 1878).

By 1906, however, Barrett implied that the Wood White was becoming scarcer, as he gave an 1855 date only for its occurrence at Exeter, and an 1859 date at Stoke, near Barnstaple. Nevertheless, he did say, that it was still to be found 'in abundance' on the cliffs east of Sidmouth, and between there and Beer, flying on broken slopes of the cliff, and even over the shingle down to the sea.

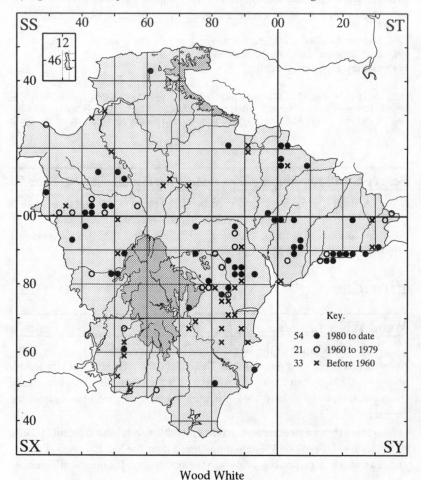

Wood White

Other localities mentioned by Barrett were Bickleigh Vale, Bridestowe, Catshill, Holsworthy, Honiton, Instow, Newnham Park, Teignmouth (in 1890), Tiverton, Torquay, and Woodbury.

Heath (1946) stated that the Wood White was local and rather scarce, but that it sometimes occurred as singletons in isolated localities. He listed, with manuscript additions, 14 localities where it had been seen, principally during the 1930s and up to 1946.

Stidston (1952) stated that it was 'formerly not uncommon, but of late years has become scarce or absent from its former haunts. It is still found sparsely in a number of widely separated districts, but as the species is considered in need of protection, localities are witheld'.

The status of the Wood White in Devon is uncertain. There are strong colonies along the East Devon cliffs and on the Haldon Hills. Elsewhere, the size and strength of the colonies are unknown. We have had a number of reports, mostly singletons, of Wood Whites from a number of localities throughout the county. Some of these turned out to be misidentifications, others, because of the late date of sighting, we suspect to be also misidentified. Nevertheless, there remain several which, although unconfirmed, may be genuine. However, even if genuine, it does not mean that there is a colony in those areas, as singletons have been recorded before in many isolated localities (Heath, 1946). Local expansions of its range still take place - for example it turned up at Hawkchurch, near Axminster, in 1971 (K.A. Gosling), but has not been seen there since 1975. It appeared in Ashclyst Forest in 1981 (T. Jenkyn). As the Wood White is commonly restricted to small areas in any one locality, it may be under-recorded.

Below, are all the known occurrences of the Wood White in Devon. Grid references are omitted for the generalised localities.

**Ashburton**, 1926, E.D. Morgan (Dev. Ass.). **Ashclyst Forest** [SY0099], breeding colony, first recorded May 29th 1981, T. Jenkyn. '**Axminster**'. We suspect that 'Axminster' of Reading (1862) should be Axmouth. A manuscript addition to Heath's (1946) list gives 'Axminster landslip'. **Axmouth-Lyme Regis cliffs** [SY2689 to 3291], part of the Sidmouth-Branscombe-Beer colonies (see also Bindon Cliff; Charton Bay). One of its strongholds. **Aylesbeare Common** [SY0690], see remarks under Woodbury. A breeding colony.

'**Barnstaple**' (Mathew, 1860). **Beer Head, Beer** [SY2188], an eastward continuation of the Branscombe colonies. **Berry Pomeroy**, (Reading, 1862). **Bickington**, June 1949, H. Dewey (Stidston, 1950). **Bickleigh (Shaugh Bridge)**, (Reading, 1862). **Bickleigh Vale** (Barrett, 1906) - probably includes the area - Cann Wood - Great Shaugh Wood (q.v.) - Shaugh Bridge. **Bindon Cliffs** [SY2689; 2789], part of the Axmouth-Lyme Regis colonies. **Black Torrington (near)**, July 8th 1968, H.A. Kennard (Dev. Ass.). **Blackawton (Longwells Wood)** [SX8051], unconfirmed sighting on June 6th 1987, C.J. Lavington-Evans. **Blackpool Corner** [SY3398], one caught in 1970, K.M. White. **Bovey Heathfield**, 1951, A.H. Dobson; May 22nd 1955, S.T. Stidston. **Bovey Tracey**, 1918 and 1922; 1957, S.T. Stidston. **Branscombe, Branscombe West, Branscombe Mouth and Branscombe Undercliff** [SY1888 to 2088], this stretch of the cliffs, which continues westwards towards Sidmouth, has always been a Wood White stronghold. It is probable that 'Sidmouth' of the older literature refers to Branscombe. The oldest specific reference to Branscombe is in 1914 (Tait, 1915). **Bridestowe**, Barrett (1906). **Brixham (South Down cliff top)** [SX9254], July 24th 1992, M. Edwards. **Broomsmead, near Lapford** [SS7510], May 15th 1925, Gay Colln. (RAMM). **Brownsham - Mouth Mill** [SS2926], July 17th 1974, T. Jenkyn. **Buckfastleigh**, Reading (1862). **Buckland in the Moor** [SX7272], unconfirmed sighting, June 16th 1985, J.A. Lindley.

**Bugford Valley, near Combe Martin** [SS6042], unconfirmed reports for 1974 to 1977, T. Beer.

**Charton Bay, Rousdon** [SY3090], part of the Axmouth - Lyme Regis colonies. June 19th 1985, N. Barns. **Christow (area)**, 1963 (Dev. Ass.). **Chudleigh** - this name in the older literature (Reading, 1862) probably refers to Chudleigh Knighton Heath. **Chudleigh Knighton Heath** [SX8377]. Although probably never absent from this area, there is a gap between a 1976 'Chudleigh' record and the sighting of at least two on June 19th 1988, D.R. Tye. See also Finlake. **Clay Moor** [SS5012], July 1st 1992, W.H. Tucker. **Clearbrook, near Yelverton** [SX5266], June 1970 (Monks Wood, BRC). **Coleford, near Stoodleigh** *[SS9019]*. According to G.M. Spooner (*pers. commn.*), this is the 'Tiverton' of J. Harvey (Blundell's School Magazine) where it was seen for the first time on May 14th 1950. **Common Moor, Hollocombe** [SS3601], 1979 (Monks Wood, BRC). **Cookworthy (near)** [SS4101], June 11th 1992, W.H. Tucker. **Cookworthy (Morcombe Plantation)** [SS4101], June 25th 1984, M.S. Warren. **Cookworthy Moor Plantation** [SS4101], common on June 29th 1974, T. Jenkyn. **Crediton (near)** [=Lapford?], Aug. 5th 1942 (Stroyan, 1942). **Cullompton**, C.W. Bracken, 'once' (Heath, 1946).

**Dalwood Hill, Dalwood** [SY2399], several, May 22nd-June 7th 1987, G.M. Chapman. **Dart, River (banks of)**, (Morris, 1876). **Dartmoor**. 1928, S.T. Stidston (Dev. Ass.). **Dunscombe (Dunscombe Cliffs)** [SY1688], part of the Sidmouth-Branscombe colonies. **Dunsdon Farm NNR** [SS2806-2808], 1992, K. Bastow. **Dunsford Reserve, Dunsford** *[SX8088]*, June 13th 1970, C.W.D. Gibson (Dev. Ass.). **Dunsford (Steps Bridge)**, June 5th 1936, S.T. Stidston.

**Eggesford (Eggesford House)** *[SS6711]*, 1932, R.J. Burton; June 2nd 1934, common, M.G. Palmer (Doe, 1941). **'Exeter'** of Reading (1862) and Barrett (1906) is almost certainly a general locality, and probably refers to Stoke Woods or Ashclyst Forest.

**Finlake, Chudleigh** [SX8578], June 9th 1985, D.J. Hopkins. None seen by D. Smallshire on May 19th and 25th 1989. **Fordlands** *[SX8690]*, June 2nd 1910, F. Blanchford (Dev. Ass.).

**Haldon (Kiddens Plantation and Tower Wood)**, a thriving colony. Although Wood Whites have been known on the Haldon Hills from at least the 1950s (see Harcombe House), their recent success is almost certainly due to 'coniferisation' and the maintenance of wide open rides. **Halwill Moor Plantation** [SS4200], June 26th 1976, W.H. Tucker. **Hannicombe Wood, near Drewsteignton** [SX7489], unconfirmed sighting July 11th 1987, J.A.S. Newman. **Harcombe House, Haldon Moor** *[?SX8981]*, one male, June 1st 1955, B.P. Braden. **Harpford Wood, Harpford** *[SY1090]*, pre-1946, R.M. Prideaux (Heath, 1946). **Hartland** - 1969, A.P. Gainsford (Dev. Ass.). **Hawkchurch** [ST3400], first seen June 22nd 1971, K.A. Gosling; seen again in 1975, but not subsequently. **Hawkerland Valley, Hawkerland** [SY0589], there is an established colony in this area. **Haydon, near Kenton** [SX9283], '90% certain of identification', June 16th 1989, P. Butter. **Heathfield**. A generalised locality that probably extends from Bovey to Stover (see also Bovey Heathfield). There are records for July 21st and 28th 1934, H. Henstock, 1947 and 1951, A.H. Dobson; May 5th and June 6th 1957 (Dev. Ass.) and June 18th 1967 (Monks Wood BRC). **Highampton (Coombe Farm SSSI)** [SS4902], 3 females ovipositing June 22nd, 1989, G.J. Barnes. **Hole** [SS4603], this colony, seen by T. Jenkyn on July 3rd 1974, may have moved into the area along the old railway line (now badly overgrown). The owner is reported to have seen the Wood White in 1989, K. Bastow. **Hole Farm** [SS4602], June 3rd 1992, W.H. Tucker. **Hollow Moor** [SS4701], 1979 (NCC). **Holsworthy**, July 2nd 1934, H. Henstock (Dev. Ass.). **Holwill** [SS4210], July 16th 1991, H. Marshall. **Honiton**. Barrett's (1906) 'Honiton' is almost certainly a generalised one. **Huntsham** [ST0020], Aug. 6th 1989, R. Greenwood.

**Ide, Exeter**, 1906 (Dev. Ass.). **Instow**, April 24th 1893, K.M. Hinchcliff (RAMM). **Ipplepen**, Reading (1862).

**Kenton (Oxton)** *[SX9282]*, May 11th 1895 (Studd Collection). **Kingford Fen, Pancrasweek** [SS2806], a colony discovered by K. Bastow in 1987. **Kingsbridge** [SX7640], 1990, O. Knight. **Kingskerswell**, 1910, J. Walker (Dev. Ass.). **Kingsteignton (clay pits)** - 'a rough field which fringes a large pond on the left of the Chudleigh-Newton Abbot road', S.T. Stidston (Dev. Ass.) *[SX8474]*, May 9th 1934; July 26th 1935, S.T. Stidston. **Kingston** [SX6248], one mile from River Erme, east bank, August 1963 (Monks Wood, BRC).

**Langtree, near Great Torrington** [SS4513], unconfirmed sighting July 20th 1988, K. Duncan. **Lapford district**, probably a generalised locality, but may refer to Bowerthy Wood to the north-west. A specimen in the Gay Colln., RAMM, is dated June 1st 1920. **Lincombe Mouth** [SY1587], part of the Sidmouth - Branscombe colonies. **Longdown** *[SX8691]*, pre-1946, R.M. Prideaux (Heath, 1946); 1969, one in the garden of D.W. Mitchell (Dev. Ass.). **Lustleigh (R. Bovey)** [SX7880], Aug. 12th 1990, S.E. Moore. **Lydford** [SX5083], May 28th

1990, T.D. Sleep and A.R. Hawtin, and July 2nd 1992, N. Baldock; [SX4983] June 6th 1993, T.D. Sleep and A.R. Hawtin.

**Marystow** [SX4283], Sept. 1st 1969, one male, C.J.A. Craik (Dev. Ass.). **Aylesbeare (Manor Plantation)** [SY0490], June 6th 1986, G.H. Gush. **Mouth Mill** - see Brownsham.

**Newton Abbot**. This is possibly the Bradley Wood locality (see below) - seen on June 6th 1925 (Dev. Ass.). **Newton Abbot (Bradley Wood)** *[SX8470]*, c.1924, E.D. Mitchell (Dev. Ass.). **Newton Abbot (Milber Down)**, noted in 1868 (Dev. Ass.). **Newton Ferrers**, Aug. 8th 1948, O.D. Hunt (Dev. Ass.). **Newton St Cyres**, unconfirmed, but not unexpected sightings in Coombland Wood [SX8796] in 1988 and 1989, E. Endacott, and Northridge Copse [SX8586], May 31st 1987, Mr Michelmore. **Northlew**, 1888 (Monks Wood, BRC).

**Oakford**, 1941, common, E.M. Kelly (Doe, 1942); also recorded (under 'Tiverton') in 1949 (Stidston, 1950). **Okehampton** - a generalised locality referred to by H.L.G. Stroyan (1942).

**Petrockstow Moor** [SS5210], July 1st 1980, M.S. Warren. **Plympton (Great Shaugh Wood)** [SX5260], July 9th 1983, T.D. Sleep; one only, Aug. 13th 1986, V.R. Tucker. **Plympton (Plym Bridge)**, Reading (1862). **Plymstock**, July 1921, S.T. Stidston (Dev. Ass.). **Preston**, May 1933, G.F.B. Prior (Heath, 1946).

**Rackenford Moor** [SS8521], c.1983, P. Allfrey.

**Salcombe Regis** [SY1587], part of the Sidmouth - Branscombe colonies. **Sandygate**, c.1924 (Torquay Nat. Hist. Soc.). **Sampford Peverell**, May 13th and June 6th 1950, F.H. Lyon (Dev. Ass.) (see also Uplowman). **Sidmouth**. Sidmouth of the older literature probably refers to the cliffs east of Sidmouth - up to and possibly including Branscombe. One of the earliest records that we have for this area is a specimen caught in 1892 (Fenwick Colln., RAMM). It was described as abundant by Barrett (1906). Recorded at Sidmouth by R.J. Heckford on July 29th 1971. **Sillick Moor, Holsworthy** [SS3300], August 1967 (Monks Wood BRC). **Sourton, Okehampton** [SX5389], May 1982, R. & E. Hart. **Sowton Hill, Dunsford** [SX8288], June 1968 (Monks Wood, BRC). **Stadson Bridge, Black Torrington** [SS4304], July 1968, H.A. Kennard (Dev. Ass.). **Stagg Mill, Uplowman** [ST0016], Aug. 6th 1989, R. Greenwood. **Staple Cross, Hockworthy** [ST0320], unconfirmed sighting on July 6th 1987, M.J. Lee. **Stoodleigh** - see Coleford. **Stover Park**, June 6th 1925 (Torquay Nat. Hist. Soc.); 1951, A.H. Dobson (Dev. Ass.).

**Tavistock (near)**, June 30th 1940, F.W. Jeffery (Heath, 1946). **Tiverton**. A generalised locality; older records probably refer to the woods along the Exe valley; E.M. Kelly's, and some of the Blundell School records, concern the Oakford area (Stidston, 1949; G.M. Spooner, *pers. commn.*). **Torbryan**, c.1924, E.D. Morgan (Torquay Nat. Hist. Soc.). **Torquay**. Reading (1862) and Barrett (1906). An early record of J. Walker (in Heath, 1946) stated that it was fairly plentiful, but local. **Torrington**, May 1893, Miss K.M. Hinchcliff (RAMM).

**Ugbrooke**, c.1924, E.D. Morgan (Torquay Nat. Hist. Soc.). **Under Hooken** [SY2188], the eastern continuation of the Branscombe colonies. **Upcott, near Hatherleigh** [SS5703], June 25th 1973 (B.P. Braden diaries). **Uplowman** [ST0015], unconfirmed, rather late, sighting on Aug. 27th 1986, R. Greenwood (see also Sampford Peverell).

**Venn Ottery Common** [SY0691], 1984; a female, July 4th 1985, and two, May 21st 1988, G.H. Gush.

**Weston Mouth, Weston** [SY1688], part of the Sidmouth-Branscombe colonies. **Westward Ho! (cliffs)**, 1898 (Dev. Ass.). **Whitestone (1km north of)** [SX8694], July 29th 1975 (B.P. Braden diaries, RAMM) (see also Newton St Cyres). **Winkleigh**, probably Winkleigh Wood *[SS6408]*, now coniferised, May 1943, W.E. Minnion (Heath, 1946). **Woodbury**. Almost certainly 'Woodbury' of the older authors is a general name for one or more of the East Devon commons (Aylesbeare, Venn Ottery and Woodbury commons, Manor Plantation, Hawkerland Valley). The earliest record that we have for this area is from Woodbury Wood, 1887 and 1888 (Sim Colln., RAMM). There are many subsequent records, including Woodbury Common on May 25th 1974, R.J. Heckford, up to the present day.

**Yarner Wood** [SX7878], 1967, R.V. Russell, but not in 1968-73.

The main larval foodplants are Bitter Vetch *Lathyrus montanus* and Common Birdsfoot-trefoil *Lotus corniculatus*.

The Wood White normally flies from mid- or end of May until the end of June (earliest date, April 11th 1988, M. Land). In some years (1942, 1948, 1956,

1960, 1961, 1963, 1967, 1969, 1971, 1974-1978, 1982, 1983, 1986-1989), there is a partial second brood in late July and early August. It has been recorded as late as Sept. 1st, 1969 (C.J.A. Craik, Dev. Ass.).

## Pale Clouded Yellow *Colias hyale* (Linnaeus)                 Plate 7c

A rare immigrant. Care has to be taken to distinguish the pale female form (var. *helice*) of the Clouded Yellow from the Pale Clouded Yellow; even greater care has to be excercised in separating the latter from the even rarer Berger's Clouded Yellow.

Surprisingly, in 1983, a year of a large Clouded Yellow influx, only one Pale Clouded Yellow was recorded in Devon (Plymouth), whereas, for example, 1955 was a good year for both species. Nationally, the years 1900, 1945, 1947-1949 and 1955 were good ones with over 100 sightings throughout the country.

The following are all the records for Devon:

1870, **Totnes racecourse** (common), G.C. Bignell (Parfitt, 1878).

pre-1878, **Torquay and Sidmouth**, E. Johnson; **Babbington**, Dr Battersby (Parfitt, 1878).

1889, **Sidmouth** (Majendie, 1891).

1900, **Torquay**, May, J. Walker; **Dawlish**, May, E.D. Mitchell (Stidston, 1952); **Torquay - Teignmouth road**, S.T. Stidston (Dev. Ass.).

1901, **Torquay** J. Walker (Dev. Ass.).

1903, **'South Devon'**, S.T. Stidston (Dev. Ass.).

pre-1906, **Plymouth, Dartmouth, Teignmouth, Honiton** and **Mortehoe** (Barrett, 1906)

1921; 1923 **Bickleigh Vale** and **Plymouth**; **Yealm district** (1923 only) S.T. Stidston (Dev. Ass.).

1945, **Wembury**, Aug. 2nd, D.G. Blackie (Dev. Ass.).

1947, **Ashburton**, April 24th, S.T. Stidston (two) and D. Canning (one) (Dev. Ass.); **Torre, Torquay**, Aug. 4th, E.J. Keir; **Bantham**, three on Aug. 23rd, J.L. Palmer; **Ipplepen** and **Northam Burrows**, Aug. 22nd, G.H. Gush (Dev. Ass.); **Start Point**, Aug. 16 to 18th, 'two dozen' (Dannreuther, 1948).

1949, **Newton Abbot (Milber Down)**, Sept. 6th, S.T. Stidston; **Newton Abbot (Knowles Hill)**, August, H. Dewey; **Torcross**, Aug. 13th, J.L. Palmer (Stidston, 1952).

1955, **Thurlestone**, Aug. 1st (Manley, 1955); **Sidmouth** and **Newton Poppleford** (Dev. Ass.), **Teignmouth Front** (Plate 7c), **Salcombe** and **Bishopsteignton**, no date, C.W. Holcroft (RAMM).

1966, **East Budleigh Common**, four on Sept. 12th, two on 13th, three on 15th, and two on 21st, E. Dutton; **Churston Ferrers**, Oct. 12th, D.S. Fish (Turner, 1967).

1969, **Princetown**, July 23rd, one female, F.W. Jeffery; **'south-west Devon'**, R.G.H. (Dev. Ass.).

1973, **Venn Ottery Common**, Aug. 10th, G.H. Gush.

1980, **Membury**, Sept. 21st, D.A. Rook.

1982, **Branscombe**, June 2nd, one male, E.C. Pelham-Clinton.

1983, **South Ernsettle**, Sept. 24th (Bretherton and Chalmers-Hunt, 1984).

## Berger's Clouded Yellow *Colias alfacariensis* Berger     Plate 7d

The only Devon record is a pair caught in North Devon by a Mr B. White in July 1949, and now in the collection of Mr D. Worton of East Looe, Cornwall - see plate.

# Clouded Yellow *Colias croceus* (Geoffroy)      Plate 7e

This is an irregular immigrant that occurs in most years, sometimes in abundance, such as the years 1877, 1900, 1908, 1913, 1921, 1928, 1933, 1947-1949, 1955, 1957, 1959, 1967, 1969, 1983, 1989 and 1992 of which 1947 and 1983 were exceptional. Nationally in 1947, 36,000 individuals were estimated to have occurred, whilst in 1983, the estimated number was 15,000 (Emmet and Heath, 1989). In 1983, Devon was one of the main immigration areas, with numbers thought to exceed 1000 (Bretherton and Chalmers-Hunt, 1984). Unfortunately, recording for the Devon Atlas had not begun in 1983, and the records that we have for the years 1981-1984 have been gathered retrospectively. For 1983, which are considerably below the estimate of Bretherton and Chalmers-Hunt, we had 177 records of at least 214 individuals, plus one recorders observation (and this must have been the experience of several) of '100s in one field'. The data for the period 1946 to 1970 are from the records of the Devonshire Association.

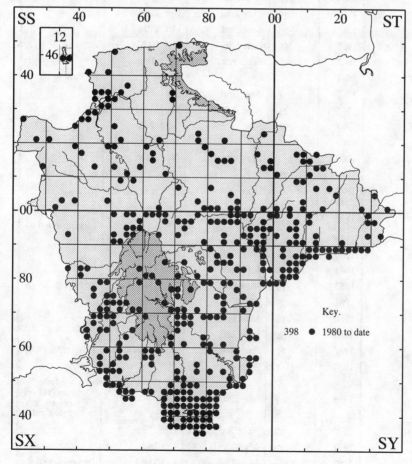

Clouded Yellow

37

| Year | Number | First date | Last date | Comment |
|---|---|---|---|---|
| 1946 | 5 | | | |
| 1947 | 5144 | June 1st | Dec. 7th | |
| 1948 | 338 | April 25th | Nov. 11th | |
| 1949 | 2003 | April 24th | Nov. 7th | 75 var. *helice* |
| 1950 | 66 | April 30th | Oct. 3rd | |
| 1951 | 14 | Aug. 6th | Oct. 9th | |
| 1952 | 96 | May 17th | Oct. 10th | 3 var. *helice* |
| 1953 | 4 | May 24th | Sept. 8th | 1 var. *helice* |
| 1954 | 47 | May 29th | Oct. 10th | |
| 1955 | 1547 | June 4th | Nov. 11th | 30 var. *helice* |
| 1956 | 24 | May 5th | Oct. 4th | |
| 1957 | 161 | mid-April | Oct. 30th | 7 var. *helice* |
| 1958 | 5 | May 17th | Sept. 9th | |
| 1959 | 111 | July 20th | Nov. 6th | 5 var. *helice* |
| 1960 | 49 | May 29th | Oct. 22nd | |
| 1961 | 20 | Sept. 2nd | Oct. 14th, | |
| 1962 | 10 | June 8th | Oct. 10th | |
| 1963 | 2 | Sept. 9th | Sept. 18th | |
| 1964 | | | | no data |
| 1965 | 4 | Aug. 2nd | Sept. 1st | |
| 1966 | 21 | June 3rd | Sept. 23rd | |
| 1967 | 172 | July 1st | Sept. 27th | |
| 1968 | 16 | July 6th | Sept. 23rd | |
| 1969 | 265 | May 1st | Nov. 14th | |
| 1970 | 22 | | | no data |
| 1971 - 1980 | | | | no data |
| 1981 and 1982 | | | | incomplete data |
| 1981 | 5 | Aug. 14th | Sept. 27th | |
| 1982 | 15 | July 25th | Oct. 15th | |
| 1983 | 214 | June 6th | Nov. 11th | but see p. 37 |
| 1984 | 25 | July 15th | Oct. 15th | |
| 1985 | 10 | May 1st | Oct. 21st | |
| 1986 | 51 | June 25th | Oct. 26th | |
| 1987 | 71 | Aug. 1st | mid-November | (Thornett, 1988) |
| 1988 | 1 | Aug. 8th | | |
| 1989 | 181 | May 29th | Oct. 29th | Main immigration began on July22nd |
| 1990 | 27 | Aug. 3rd | Nov. 17th | |
| 1991 | 22 | May 22nd | Oct 2nd | |
| 1992 | 250+ | May 15th | Oct 31st | incomplete data |

The Clouded Yellow is able to breed in this country and may produce several generations before being killed off by frost. Because of the succession of generations, the adults can occur well into November, or, if there are no frosts, December (Dec. 7th 1947). In 1947, southward return flights of the Clouded Yellow were recorded in October in Devon, at Selsey Bill, and 40 miles south of the Lizard (Stidston in Bracken, 1948).

The larval foodplants are Clovers, and Trefoils *Trifolium* spp., Kidney-vetch *Anthyllis vulneraria* and Lucerne *Medicago sativa*. White (in Turner, 1977) raised a Clouded Yellow larva from an egg laid on Crown Vetch *Coronilla varia*.

## **Brimstone** *Gonepteryx rhamni* (Linnaeus) — Plate 7f

The Brimstone is fairly common and widely distributed. It is the only non-nymphalid butterfly in Britain to overwinter as an adult. Consequently, it

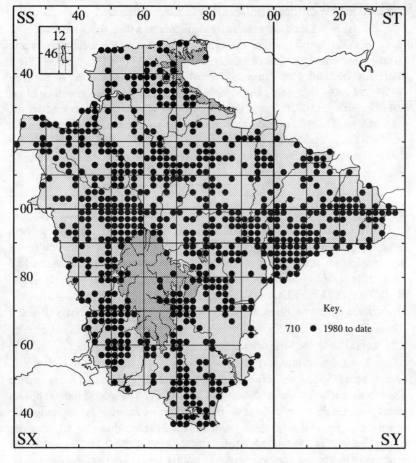

Brimstone

is one of the earliest spring butterflies to be seen - normally it flies from early April to early June. The succeeding generation appears in late July/early August until the end of September or sometimes into October before settling down for hibernation.

Buckthorn *Rhamnus catharticus* and Alder Buckthorn *Frangula alnus* are thought to be the only larval foodplants. Murdoch (1988) reported a Brimstone laying eggs on dock *Rumex* spp. in an area where there was no buckthorn; the larvae did not feed and died. Presumably, in the absence of the accepted foodplants, the female in question was desperate to lay her eggs somewhere.

A comparison of the distribution map of the Brimstone with that of its known foodplants in Devon (Ivimey-Cook, 1984) shows the wide-ranging dispersion of this species, particularly over the South Hams where its foodplants are particularly scarce.

## Black-veined White *Aporia crataegi* (Linnaeus)

This species died out in Devon long before its national extinction in 1922. Its former distribution within the county is unknown. Pratt (in Emmet and Heath, 1989) stated that it became scarce at Plymouth after 1826. In 1854, it was abundant at Castle Hill, Torquay (Barrett, 1893), and, according to Stainton (1857), 'tolerably common' at Moretonhampstead. A supposed specimen in the Dale Collection, Oxford, from 'Harford, Devon' (Pratt, in Emmet and Heath, 1989), does not exist. We believe that 'Harford' is a mistranscription of Hereford, of which there is such a labelled specimen in the collection. There are no other data for the species in Devon. It appears to have become extinct by 1862 (Reading, 1862).

## Large White *Pieris brassicae* (Linnaeus)                    Plate 8a

This is a common and one of the most widely distributed butterflies in Devon. It probably occurs in every tetrad, with the possible exception of the higher parts of Dartmoor. It is common in urban areas where brassicas and Nasturtium *Tropaeolum majus*, the larval foodplants, are grown in gardens and allotments. In Devon, Large White larvae have been recorded on Watercress *Nasturtium officinale*, Black Mustard *Brassica nigra*, Wild Cabbage *Brassica oleracea*, Hedge Mustard *Sisymbrium officinale*, Sea Radish *Raphanus raphanistrum* and Horse Radish *Armoracia rusticana*.

The Large White is double, sometimes triple-brooded (as in 1989). In normal years the spring brood emerges in mid- to late May, and in favourable years much earlier (March 15th in 1945, F.W. Jeffery). The second brood appears about two months later. In good years, a third brood emerges in late September or early October and, with good weather, will fly throughout the latter month (up to Oct. 31st in 1989, H. Marshall, but Nov. 18th 1990, R.H. Newland). The progeny of this brood may overwinter in milder areas either as larvae or pupae.

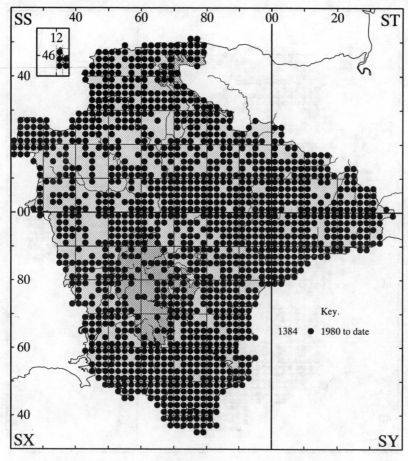

Large White

The Large White population is commonly reinforced by immigration from the Continent.

---

## Small White *Pieris rapae* (Linnaeus)        Plate 8b

Similar remarks apply to this species as to the Large White, although the Small White has been recorded on fewer tetrads than the Large White. Larvae have been found in Devon on Lesser Swine Cress *Coronofus didymus* and Watercress *Nasturtium officinale*.

It usually emerges 2 to 3 weeks earlier and is usually seen from late April onwards. Exceptionally, as in 1989 and 1990, it occurs in March, and was recorded on Feb. 24th in 1974 (Skinner, 1974). The latest recorded date is Nov. 3rd 1986, M. Wright.

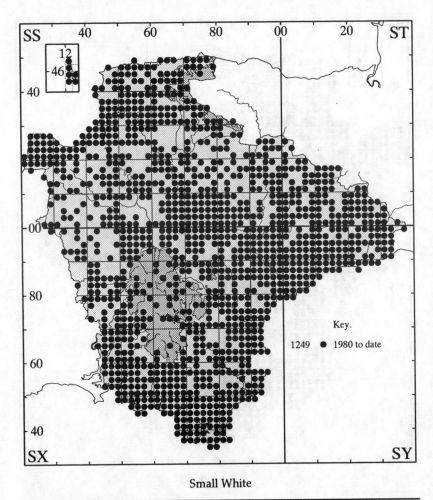

Small White

## Green-veined White *Pieris napi* (Linnaeus)      Plate 8c

Although generally classified as a 'Cabbage White', the foodplants commonly include *Cardamine* spp., particularly *C. pratensis* (Lady's Smock or Cuckoo-flower), and less commonly Charlock *Sinapis arvensis*, Garlic Mustard *Alliaria petiolata* and Watercress *Nasturtium* spp. As with the Large and Small whites, it is widespread and probably occurs on all tetrads throughout the county, except for the higher parts of Dartmoor, although it is more a species of hedgerows and lanes.

It normally flies from mid-April (exceptionally late March - March 15th in 1949, F.W. Jeffery). There are usually only two broods; it generally disappears earlier than the other two whites, and is rarely seen after mid-September, but sometimes it flies until the second week of October (Oct. 29th, 1980, A. Archer-Lock, 1980c).

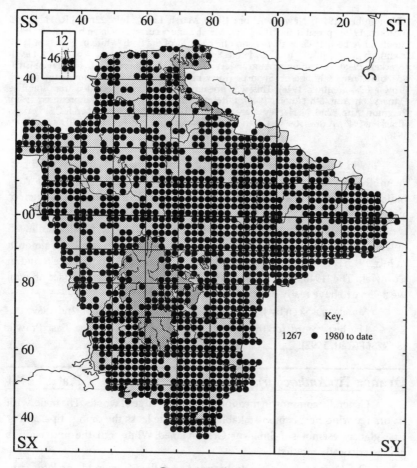

Green-veined White

## Bath White *Pontia daplidice* (Linnaeus)                    Plate 8d

The first record of this species in Devon was in October 1836 in Rosebery Wood, near Exeter, by R. Dawson (Lighton, 1843). The only other nineteenth century record was an unusually early occurrence in May (Barrett, 1893) - possibly the Culver locality of his 1906 list. The Bath White was not seen again until August 1930, when two were recorded at Plymouth by F.W. Frohawk (Stidston, 1952). There was then no further sighting until 1945, the great Bath White year, when they were seen in numbers throughout Great Britain. The following is a chronological list of all those seen during that year in Devon:

Exmouth, July 14th, W.L. Stubbs (Dannreuther, 1946). Plymouth, July 16th, R.A. Jackson (one worn) (Riley in Blathwayt, 1945). ?Noss Mayo, two, July 16th, D. Gilbert (Perkins, 1945). Plymouth, July 20th, F.W. Jeffery (Bracken, 1946). Exeter, July 17th, A. Clayton; three, Aug. 3rd; five, Aug. 28th, D.M. Sterling, and three on Aug. 30th (Dannreuther, 1946). Poltimore Village, July 17th, A.N. Coulson (Bracken, 1946). Abbotsham Cliffs [SS4127], 7 males and 5 females, July 17th - 24th, E.H. Wild (1945). Strete, July 18th, A.W.C. Smithes

43

(Dannreuther, 1946). **Newton Abbot (Jetty Marsh Lane)**, July 22nd, J.R. Heywood (Bracken, 1946) - possibly the '1946' Jetty Marsh Lane occurrence related by Bastow (1990) should have been 1945, as there is no other record of the Bath White in Devon in 1946. **Wembury**, three, July 27th, O.D. Hunt; Sept. 5th, F.W. Jeffery, and Sept. 9th, J. Heath (Bracken, 1946). **Teignmouth**, Aug. 2nd, W.G. Coldrey (Dannreuther, 1946). **Haven Cliff, Axmouth**, Aug. 6th, one, A. Swincoe (Riley in Blathwayt, 1945). **Kenton**, Aug. 6th, G. Browse (Dannreuther, 1946). This was presumably the female recorded from the 'Exe Estuary' on Aug. 6th (Anon., 1946). **Filleigh**, Aug. 11th, T. Loyd (Dannreuther, 1946). **Paignton**, Aug. 22nd, N. Harvey (Dannreuther, 1946). **Lydford**, September, R.C.L. Perkins (Bracken, 1946). **Axminster**, Oct. 10th, caught in a spider's web, E.A. Heslop (Dannreuther, 1946).

Wild (1945) thought that the large numbers that he had seen at Abbotsham, the fact that some specimens were very fresh, and others were *in cop.*, indicated that this was a breeding colony that had survived the winter of 1944/45. Although there is no conclusive evidence that the species bred in Devon, and survived into 1946 (see below), it did so in Cornwall. Kettlewell (1946) recorded wild ova on Hedge Mustard *Sisymbrium officianale* at Falmouth in July 1945; Richardson (1947) recorded breeding in 1946 from pupae found in Cornwall. The '1946' Jetty Marsh Lane, Newton Abbot, specimen (see above), we believe to have really occurred in 1945.

A male was seen by J. Kingsley Smith at Torquay on June 2nd 1969.

The last record for the county was on Aug. 4th 1991 at East Prawle [SX7736] (Catt, 1992).

---

# Orange Tip *Anthocharis cardamines* (Linnaeus)     Plates 8e, 8f

Generally common in meadows, lanes and edge of woods. The male, with its orange wing tips, is unmistakable. The female lacks the orange tips, and at first glance resembles a Small or Green-veined White, but the underside is characteristically mottled.

The Orange Tip is single brooded and flies from mid- or late April (exceptionally late March - March 17th, 1990, R.H. Newland), until the middle of June. In 1986, a partial second brood emerged - adults were seen in July (B. Price) and August (J.M. Cook and S.P. Simmonds).

The larval foodplants are Garlic Mustard *Alliaria petiolata*, Hedge Mustard *Sisymbrium officinale* and Lady's Smock *Cardamine pratense*. Searching the foodplants, particularly Garlic Mustard, for eggs and larvae can be a very effective way of recording this species, irrespective of the weather conditions. Females frequently follow roadside hedgerows and will often oviposit on isolated plants. The ova are laid on the peduncles or flower stalks; initially they are cream, but change to bright orange. Larvae at all instars feed on the developing seedpods, lying along the length of the pod and feeding on the distal end. Late deveolpers have been found on leaf or shoot buds when the seedpods have hardened.

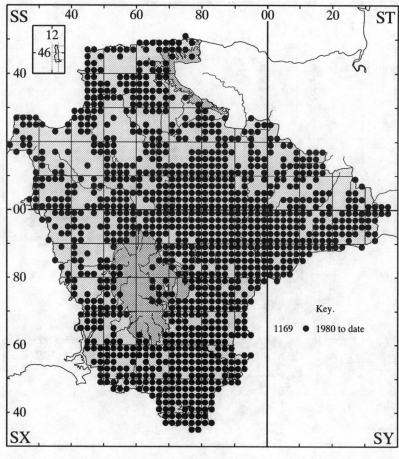

Orange Tip

# Lycaenidae

## Green Hairstreak *Callophrys rubi* (Linnaeus)      Plate 9a

Parfitt (1878) stated that 'this beautiful little butterfly is very generally distributed' and recorded seeing 'some scores' on Haldon. Stidston (1952) stated that it was the commonest hairstreak and widely distributed. In particular, 'it favours sheltered valleys on Dartmoor'. The above remarks are still generally true, although possibly the Purple Hairstreak is the commonest Devon hairstreak. From the map, it can be seen that it is most common along the coasts, with a concentration inland in South Devon, particularly around Dartmoor and the East Devon commons.

It was recorded on Lundy for the first time on June 22nd 1983 by A.J. Parsons.

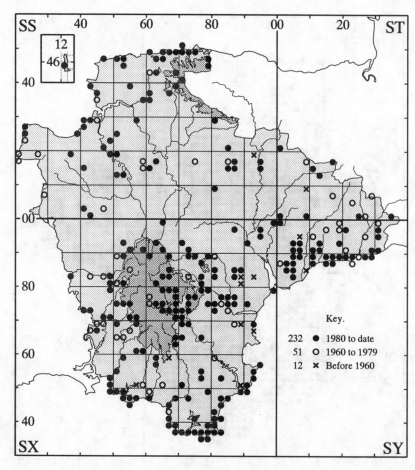

Green Hairstreak

The larvae feed on several foodplants. Nationally, these include Common Rockrose *Helianthemum chamaecistus*, Gorse *Ulex* spp., Broom *Sarothamnus scoparius*, Common Birdsfoot-trefoil *Lotus corniculatus*, Dyer's Greenweed *Genista tinctoria*, Bilberry *Vaccinium myrtillus*, and the flower buds of Buckthorn *Rhamnus catharticus* and Dogwood *Swida sanguinea* (Porter and Emmet, in Emmet and Heath, 1989).

The Green Hairstreak generally flies from mid-May until the end of June, or sometimes early July. The earliest and latest dates are April 1st 1990 (M. Catt) and August 5th 1989 (R.C. Thornett).

## Brown Hairstreak *Thecla betulae* (Linnaeus)          Plates 9b, 9c

Parfitt (1878) gave a wide scatter of localities across Devon at which *betulae* had been recorded. Stidston (1952) remarked that 'it is frequent, widely distributed, but local, favouring the river valleys running down from the moors'.

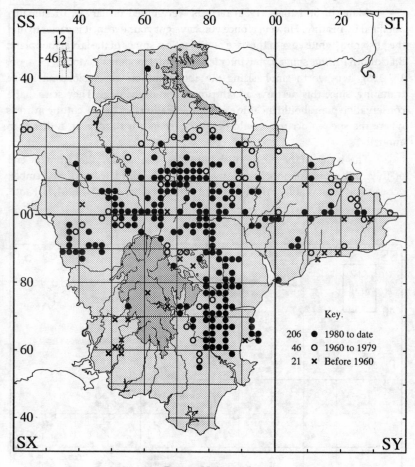

Brown Hairstreak

The first part of the statement is probably still true, but the second part has not been substantiated during the last five years. At the time of publication (1986) of the first Provisional Atlas, it seemed as though the Brown Hairstreak was dominantly a butterfly of mid-Devon. However, this was due to recording bias, as most North Devon records resulted from a concerted search by Dr T.W. Tolman for the eggs during the winter of 1980. Since that time, because of diligent searches for eggs by several recorders, we now have many more records from South Devon, and latterly even more from mid-Devon due to searching by S.G. Madge in the winter of 1992/3. From the map, the Brown Hairstreak appears to be largely absent from north-west and south-west (including Dartmoor) Devon. However, the Brown Hairstreak requires careful searching to find the adult. For much of their time, adults stay in or around the tree tops, and only descend to hedge level to oviposit, or nectar.

Many of Stidston's (1952) records were based on larvae, presumably obtained by beating. However, once you have got your eye in, it is easier to find the glistening white eggs at the base of the leafless spines of the larval foodplant, Blackthorn *Prunus spinosa*, in winter (see Pollard, Hooper and Moore, 1974, pp. 157-158). It is worth emphasising the above authors conclusions on hedge trimming, since this destroys a high proportion of the eggs. They state that a conservation plan should include a recommendation that hedge cutting in areas where the species occurs, should be every second or third year, rather than annually.

This is one of the latest British butterflies to appear; it flies from the end of July, but more commonly in August, until the third week of September; occasionally, it may still be flying in October (latest date, Nov. 1st 1984, H. King).

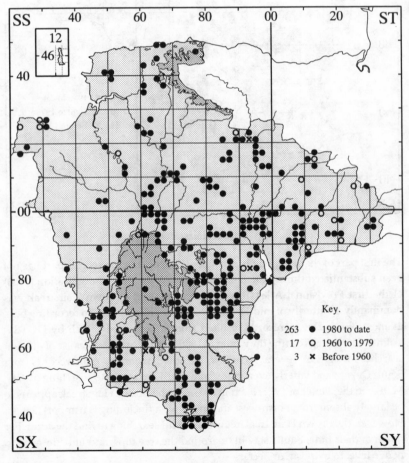

Key.

| | | |
|---|---|---|
| 263 | ● | 1980 to date |
| 17 | O | 1960 to 1979 |
| 3 | ✕ | Before 1960 |

Purple Hairstreak

## Purple Hairstreak *Quercusia quercus* (Linnaeus)  Plates 9d, 9e

Both Parfitt (1878) and Stidston (1952) noted that the Purple Hairstreak was generally distributed in oak woods, particularly in sheltered places. The above remarks still apply, although there is a paucity of records for north-west Devon. It is probably the commonest and most widely distributed Devon hairstreak, and probably occurs wherever there are a number of oaks, the larval foodplants, even along roads with widely spaced trees. They often fly until dusk, at which time they can be fairly easily found, but it generally takes a lot of neck craning to spot them fluttering around the tree tops. At times during the day, they might occur lower down, and occasionally they can be found on the ground at damp patches.

The adult usually flies from mid-July until the end of August or the beginning of September. The earliest and latest dates are June 24th 1989 (R.J. Clarke) and Sept. 27th in 1983 (Q. Paynter).

Parfitt (1878) bred the Purple Hairstreak from larvae obtained in Stoke Woods, Exeter. It remained in the pupal stage for three weeks and emerged in the first week in July. In a letter to the late F.W. Jeffery in 1957, the correspondent (undecipherable signature) wrote that he reared a Purple Hairstreak from a larva swept from Birch.

## White-letter Hairstreak *Satyrium w-album* (Knoch)  Plate 9f

Nationally, the White-letter Hairstreak has become rare because of the loss of its foodplants, elm *Ulmus* spp. Colonies can survive on elm suckers- Wych Elm *U. glabra* and Smooth-leaved Elm *U. minor*; but in Devon the only proven breeding colonies are on flowering Wych Elm.

This was one of the last native butterflies to be discovered in Devon, being found in 1907 at Ilsham by J. Walker (Lupton, 1911; Stidston, 1952), although it was possibly known to Morris (1876) under the name Black Hairstreak.

There are five colonies where breeding has been confirmed by finding eggs. All were discovered during winter 92/93. Two of these colonies were previously unsuspected, and there is a strong possibility of more at several other places described below.

It can be seen from the map that the White-letter Hairstreak is largely confined to south and east Devon, but the 1919 and 1990 records near Lynmouth suggests an extant although unconfirmed colony in North Devon. There is sufficient flowering Wych Elm near Lynmouth to support a colony.

Below are set out all the Devon occurrences of the White-letter Hairstreak:

Ashburton [SX7468], 1943; 1944, O.D. Hunt (in Stidston, 1952). **Ashclyst Forest** [SY0098], June 29th 1976, T. Jenkyn; August 1976, D. Pickering.

**Berry Pomeroy (Wood)** [SX8362], July 6th, M. Catt. **Bovey Tracey**, July 4th 1926 (Prideaux, 1929). **Bridford** [SX8286], 1991, R. Kahn. **Brixham** [SX9256], 1976, D.S. Fish (Dev. Ass.). **Broadhempston** [SX7866], 1980 (BRC, Monks Wood). **Bugford Valley, near Combe Martin** [SS6042], unconfirmed sightings 1974 to 1977, T. Beer. **Buckfastleigh** [SX7466], July 26th 1955 (Western Morning News).

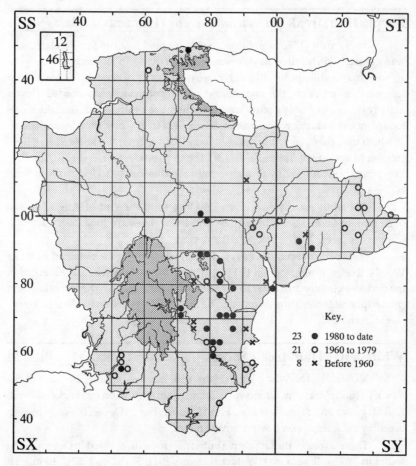

White-letter Hairstreak

**Canonteign (Barton Down)** [SX8282], Aug. 10th 1979 (BRC, Monks Wood). **Chudleigh**, 1930 (Anon., 1931). **Chudleigh (Chudleigh Rocks)** [SX8678], 1977 (BRC, Monks Wood); 1987, R. Khan; egg present Dec. 19th 1992, T.D. Sleep. **Chudleigh Knighton Heath** [SX8376], early 80's, J. & J. Woodland. **Churston Ferrers, near Brixham** [SX9054], July 1969, D.S. Fish (Turner, 1970). **Coleford, near Crediton** [SS7701], 1992, R. Kahn. **Coleridge Wood, near Dunsford** [SX7688], July 30th 1983, A. Worth. **Colyton**, 1970s (BRC, Monks Wood).

**Dartington** [SX7862], 1960 (BRC, Monks Wood); August 12th 1973, F.W. Jeffery; [SX8062], 1980 to 1982, P. Jeffery. **Dawlish Warren** [SX9878], July 31st 1980, R. Weaving and P. Nicholson. **Dunsford** [SX7889], early 80's, J. & J. Woodland.

**Exeter (Cheynegate Lane, Pinhoe)** [SX9494], early 1970s, R.J. Clarke. **Exeter (Stoke Woods)** [SX9296], July 6th 1976 (Speed, 1977); (at a mercury vapour light), 1977, H.T. King.

**Hawkchurch** [ST3400], July 17th 1970, Aug. 3rd 1972, and July 29th 1973, K.A. Gosling. **Hawkswood**, 1975, J.R.W. Coxhead (Wallace, 1979). **Hennock (Great Rock Plantation)** [SX8281], eggs present Jan. 1993, S.H. Mitchell. **Higher Metcombe** [SY0692], Aug. 10th 1980 (BRC, Monks Wood).

**Lustleigh** [SX7880], Aug. 10th 1979 (BRC, Monks Wood). **Lynmouth**, July 1919 (Randall Parkes, 1929, p.223). **Lynmouth (Myrtleberry Cleave)** [SS7248], July 17th 1990, B. Chatfield (Plate 9f).

Manaton [SX7480], 1926, R.N. Prideaux (Dev. Ass.). **Membury (Waterhouse Farm)** [ST2603], 1972, S. Glover (Wallace, 1979).

**New Bridge, Holne** [SX7070], Aug. 29th 1983, S.E. Moore. **Newton Abbot** [SX8670], larvae, 1918 and 1919, B.J. Constance (Stidston, 1952); c.1930 (Perkins, 1946). **Newton Abbot (Decoy)** [SX8670], July 20th 1990, D. Smallshire. **Newton Abbot (Broadridge and Bradley Woods)** [SX8270-8470], eggs found Dec. 13th 1992, this may be the source of the Decoy individual, S.H. Mitchell. Adult seen July 6th 1993, M. Catt.

**Ottery St Mary** [SY0894], July 1954, A.W. Piercy (Stidston, 1955).

**Phoenix Hayes**, 1974, S. Glover, N. Venn. **Plympton (Chaddlewood)** [SX5454], July 1st 1976, A. Archer-Lock. **Plympton (Linketty Lane)** [SX5256], July 23rd 1952 (Dev. Ass.); 1960 (BRC, Monks Wood); Aug. 8th 1965, F.W. Jeffery; 1976 (BRC, Monks Wood). **Plympton (Plym Bridge)** [SX5258], 1977 (BRC, Monks Wood). **Plympton (Plymbridge Wood)** [SX5258], July 10th 1976, V.R. Tucker; July 16th 1978, July 17th 1979, A. Archer-Lock; three adults, July 1989, M. Olver. **Plymstock** [SX5052], July 27th 1979, A. Archer-Lock. **Plymstock (Saltram Estate)** [SX5254], adults, 1992, M. Oates; breeding confirmed by finding eggs, Nov. 11th 1992, S.H. Mitchell and T.D. Sleep.

**Sidmouth (near the Bowd Inn)** [SY1090], July 1985, R. Newland. **Slapton** [SX8244], July 1971, G.A. Cole, and C. Tyler Smith (Turner, 1973). **Spitchwick, Holne** [SX7070], c.1983, W. Harley. **Starcross** [SX9680], July 26th 1933 (Studd Collection, RAMM). **Stoneycombe** [SX8666], eggs present, Jan. 3rd 1993, S.H. Mitchell.

**Tiverton (near)**, 1944, O.D. Hunt (Stidston, 1952); Aug. 8th 1957, G. Maunder, (Stidston, 1958). **Torquay (Ilsham Valley)** [SX9066], 1907 (Lupton, 1911); larvae plentiful in 1908, 'none seen since' (Walker, 1930); Aug. 13th 1953 (Dev. Ass.); 1955 or 1956; 1958 (Stidston, 1959). **Totnes** [SX8060], June 27th 1976, D.W. Mitchell (Dev. Ass.). 'half a mile south of Totnes Church' SX8058], Aug. 27th 1976; July 31st 1977, D.W. Mitchell (Dev. Ass.); 1990, M. Catt. **Totnes (Lake Garden)** [SX8058], 1980 (BRC, Monks Wood).

**Yeoford** [SX7898], 1985, J. & J. Woodland.


The White-letter Hairstreak normally flies from early July (earliest date June 27th) up to the second week in August (latest date, August 28th). Davies and Emmet (in Emmet and Heath, 1989) note that adults remain close to suitable breeding trees before they disappear/disperse. They take nectar from a wide range of flowers, but only in the early morning and later in the afternoon. The rest of their time is spent basking, or feeding from aphid honey dew, at the tops of trees. Consequently, the adults are seldom observed, even though they may be common.

Although normally regarded as a sedentary species, adults do occasionally wander, as noted by Archer-Lock (1980b) in Plymouth and Bath, and the occurrence of a specimen at Dawlish Warren (see above).

## Black Hairstreak *Satyrium pruni* (Linnaeus)

Morris (1876) recorded that Mr James Dalton had caught the Black Hairstreak at Black Hill near Exmouth. The basis for this statement is unknown, possibly it refers to the capture of a White-letter Hairstreak, which at one time was known by the name Black Hairstreak, and may have been communicated to Morris under that name.

A second reference to the species in Devon was in July 1987 (Bruce, 1987). On questioning, Bruce stated that she had seen them twice in two years, but confessed that she was not a butterfly expert. Almost certainly this was a case of misidentification - again the White-letter Hairstreak seems the most likely candidate, but that in itself would be remarkable news as there have been so few sightings of that species in Devon in the last five years.

## Small Copper *Lycaena phlaeas* (Linnaeus)    Plate 10a

The Small Copper is widely distributed, but rarely appears in large numbers. However, 1989 was an exception, with adults of the second and third brood being very common; up to 30 could be found on clumps of Fleabane and thistles. Generally, *phlaeas* is double brooded, but, as in 1989, it is sometimes triple brooded. The spring brood emerges from mid-May (occasionally at the end of April; exceptionally, Mar. 3rd 1938); the second brood appears from mid-July; the third brood from September until well into October, but it was seen on Nov. 11th in 1989 (V.R. Tucker), Nov. 5th in 1989 (T.D. Sleep) and Nov. 7th in 1988 (J. Kingsley Smith).

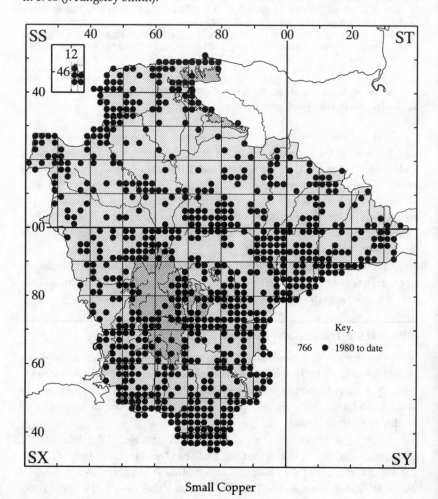

Small Copper

Larval foodplants are Sheep's Sorrel *Rumex acetosella* and Common Sorrel *R. acetosa*. Ova and larvae have been found on the former on sunny, well-drained, sandy soils. Individual plants chosen for oviposition may be very small and commonly associated with bare soil.

## Large Copper *Lycaena dispar* (Haworth)

A Large Copper, exhibited by Wentworth Buller at the Exeter Naturalists Club in 1865 (D'Urban, 1865), had been picked up amongst sedges at Slapton Ley. This presumably was the basis for the statement by Kirby (1896) 'that the last specimen recorded [in Britain] was picked up dead in Devonshire in 1865', and this may be the unspecified locality 'somewhere near the sea in the West of England' referred to by Kirby (in Merrin, 1899). Slapton Ley is one of the few areas in Devon where the larval foodplant, Great Water Dock *Rumex hydrolapathum* grows.

Allan (1980, pp. 41, 60) referred to an unspecified West Country locality for the Large Copper. In another reference to 'a large copper', it was not clear whether he thought that the large red butterfly seen by Margaret Mallock of Brampton [sic] Speke in a South Devonshire lane in 1865 (Mallock, 1865) was a Large or a Middle Copper. *R. hydrolapathum* can still be found in the Exe valley in this area.

A specimen caught by M. Gillingwater in Ashclyst Forest on Aug. 7th 1992 must have been a "release".

The nearest locality to Devon where undoubted *dispar* have been recorded is the Somerset fens, of which the last record was in 1857 (Crotch, 1857).

## Middle Copper *Lycaena virgaureae* (Linnaeus)

Allan (1980) speculated at length that large coppery butterflies seen by H.G. Mills and Mrs Castle Russell in mid-Devon in June 1917 were the Middle Copper. He also referred to another unspecified West Country locality where this species may have been seen. He noted (1980, p. 43) that there are specimens of *virgaureae* in the Castle Museum, Taunton (together with Somerset-caught *L. dispar*), but for which he gave the unsubstantiated opinion that they 'may have come from elsewhere'.

## Sooty Copper *Lycaena tityrus* (Poda)                    Plate 10b

A male of this common European species was caught at Lee, Ilfracombe, in August 1887 by C.A. Latter (Howarth, 1973). This was the first occurrence of the species in Britain (two others are now known (Emmet and Heath, 1989)). The specimen is in the Ilfracombe Museum. Burton (1992) suggested that it was a natural vagrant and not accidently imported.

## Purple-shot Copper *Lycaena alciphron* (Rottemburg)

An example of this central and southern European species, caught in July 1886, by F.G. Johnson of Blundell's School, was originally described as having been found at Tiverton (Carrington, 1887). In fact, it was caught at Sudbury, Suffolk (Barrett, 1893).

## Long-tailed Blue *Lampides boeticus* (Linnaeus)                Plate 10c

This is a scarce immigrant from southern Europe. The earliest Devon record is a specimen in the Dale Collection, Oxford, labelled 'from J.G. Ross, 1882, who had it from a boy who took it in Devonshire', to which Dale has added 'Dartmouth' (Tutt, 1908).

Subsequent records include:

**Torquay**, Sept. 2nd 1920, Col. Coleridge (Stidston, 1956).

**Torquay**, (wrongly given as Maidstone in Emmet and Heath, 1989), 3 fresh specimens between 19th and 25th Sept. 1926, and 6 after the 25th. According to Frohawk (1934:199), these were 'in the finest possible condition' and had 'evidently bred in his garden'.

**Paignton (Goods yard)**, Oct. 21st 1941 (Milman, 1942:68). This specimen is now in the Lees Collection.

**Lydford**, a worn female on candytuft, July 27th 1945 (the year of a large immigration of *L. boeticus*), R.C.L. Perkins (Perkins, 1945a).

**Axminster**, Oct. 2nd, ?1946 (Stidston, 1952:11). However, no other Long-tailed Blue was recorded that year in Britain, and as Stidston gave the Lydford date incorrectly as 1946, it seems more probable that the Axminster occurrence was part of the 1945 immigration (Bretherton, *pers. commn.*).

**Meadfoot.** The circumstances surrounding this record are suspicious. After a plant of the Broad-leaved Everlasting-pea *Lathyrus latifolius*, collected on the cliffs at Meadfoot on July 13th 1960 by W.L. Coleridge, was brought indoors to feed two surviving larvae of *boeticus* brought from the Continent (Stidston, 1961; Cribb, 1960:115-117), a total of six larvae were found. Although care had been taken to ensure that only the two surviving larvae were transferred from their original foodplant, the possibility that other larvae of continental origin were also moved unknowingly cannot be excluded.

**Kingswear**, Nov. 20th 1961, M.R. Edmonds (specimen determined by the late F.W. Jeffery) and recorded by French (1963:36).

**Prawle**, 1990-2. Contrary to the statement in Bretherton and Chalmers-Hunt (1990), M. Catt believes this to have been a genuine immigrant, and that it bred here. Larvae fed on Narrow-leaved Everlasting-pea *Lathyrus sylvestris*. But in 1992 the colony was taken by collectors, who stripping the food plants of flower buds (M. Catt, *pers. commn.*, see also Catt, 1992).

**Higher Metcombe**, Aug. 14th 1992, possible sighting, G.H. Gush.

From these records it can be seen that most occurrences are on the south coast in September and October.

## Small Blue *Cupido minimus* (Fuessly)                Plate 10d

### History and status

The status and distribution of the Small Blue in Devon has always been uncertain. Stidston (1952) thought that it became extinct in the county in about 1926. Happily, that was not so; it occurs at at least twelve sites, and possibly at four others. Colonies occur on broken cliffs and undercliffs, earthworks, old railways and dune systems. With the exception of Littleham Cove, all are found on calcareous soils. As several colonies of the Small Blue have recently been discovered, it is clear that the mapped distribution is incomplete, and that additional colonies will probably be found. It is an elusive butterfly that can easily be overlooked or confused with other species. Its diminutive size, its dull colouration and its habit of generally flying close to the ground combine to make it a difficult butterfly to spot. Size alone, however, is not a sufficient criterion for identifying a small blue butterfly as a Small Blue. The Common Blue can be as small, or in exceptional circumstances, smaller than a Small Blue. If a male, the metallic blue of the wings eliminates the Small Blue. If a female, or a Brown Argus of either sex, the orange spots or bands on both the upper and underside again rules out a Small Blue. For certain identification, you need to examine the

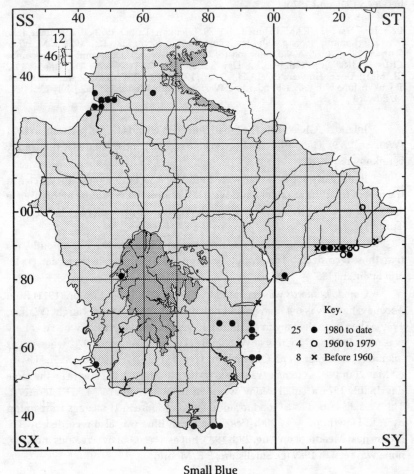

Small Blue

underside. On the Small Blue, this is silvery grey with small black dots - the only common butterfly that has a similar underside is the Holly Blue.

The first record of the Small Blue (as *alsus*) was by Jermyn (1827) on Dartmoor. It was known from the Teignmouth cliffs in the 1830s to 1850s (Turton and Kingston, 1830; Jordan; 1842; Jordan, 1843 - 'common'; Stainton, 1857 - 'common').

Reading (1862) stated that it was rare in the Plymouth district, but also gave the following localities: Meavy Vale, Dartmouth, Seaton (Z.J. Edwards) and Slapton. Morris (1876) stated that he had taken it 'in plenty' at Pinhay Cliff. The same list of localities was repeated by Parfitt (1878) and Barrett (1906). Stidston (1952) quoted a capture at Torquay in 1926 (Walker, 1930) as one of the last in the county.

From East Devon, the Small Blue has been recorded at the following localities. It is interesting to note that there was a 24-year gap in sightings between 1936 and 1970:

**Beer,** June 21st 1936 (RAMM); June 10th 1970, T. Jenkyn (Turner, 1973). **Branscombe,** June 7th 1930 (Demuth, 1985, p. 13); May 25th 1934, T. Jenkyn; May 12th 1971, K.M. White (Turner, 1973); 1972, A.N.B. Simpson (BRC, Monks Wood). **Dunscombe (Dunscombe Cliffs)** [SY1688], June 12th 1983, P.S. Day. **Seaton,** 1978, T.J. Wallace. **Sidcot,** June 5th 1922 (RAMM)). **Under Hooken,** 1971, A.H.J. Smart; 1972-1978, J.R.W. Coxhead; June 19th 1984, T. Jenkyn; June 17th 1989, J. Kenderdine. **Weston Mouth, Weston** [SY1688], July 23rd 1992, M. Edwards.

Inland, S. Glover saw the Small Blue in Wellands Copse [ST2700] in 1971 (Wallace, 1979). The site has not been visited recently and the status of this colony is unknown.

In the early 1980s, larvae were found by R.D. Sutton on Kidney Vetch at the foot of the cliffs at Littleham Cove. H. Wooltorton saw adults in this area in 1986, but none was seen on May 29th (H. Wooltorton), nor on June 15th 1989 (J. Turner).

There is no more recent record of the Small Blue in the Teignmouth area than those recorded by Turton and Kingston (1830), Jordan (1842), Jordan (1843) and Stainton (1857).

*Cupido minimus* was recorded by Barrett (1906) and Lupton (1911) from Torquay, but it was not seen again until 1926 when three were caught (Walker, 1930). There was then a gap of almost 40 years until May 1965, when a colony was recorded by P.N. Crow at Watcombe (Turner, 1966), and 1970, when it was 'plentiful', A.P. Gainsford. One male and two females were seen by A.R. Hawtin on May 20th 1990. A female was noted farther south by A.R. Hawtin on the same day. In July 1974, a 'small colony' was seen at Babbacombe by M.A. Easterbrook. This was described as a 'good locality' by S.E. Moore in 1984; eggs were found by A.R. Hawtin on May 20th 1990. The Small Blue was also recorded by S.E. Moore near Meadfoot on Aug. 29th 1983, but as a result of overzealous mowing, none was seen in 1989 (D. Smallshire; S.E. Moore).

The Small Blue used to occur near Paignton. Specimens in the Lees Colln. are dated June 13th 1926, G.P. Sutton, and May 28th 1948, P.P. Milman.

The occurrence in the Berry Head area appears to have been first noted by R.G.H. and F.W. Jeffery on May 29th and June 20th 1959 (specimen in Lees Colln.), and 1960 by M.R. Edmonds (Dev. Ass.). After a gap of twenty six years, the Small Blue was again sighted at Berry Head (both first and second broods) in 1986 (K. Tucker, N. Ward and J. Johnson), in 1987 (N. Smallbones, K. Tucker) and 1989 (C. & J. Johnson, K. Tucker and N.C. Ward). Two adult second brood were seen by M. Catt in 1990.

At Start Point, one was seen by J. Bloomfield on June 18th 1988, where she had previously seen the Small Blue 'a couple of years ago'. None was found in 1989 (J. Bloomfield and T.D. Sleep); it would appear from the distribution of the larval foodplant, that the 1988 singleton was a stray, and any colony is more likely to be located west of Start Point. Four sites between Bolt Head and Start Point are known to M. Catt (1990-2).

There is an early record of the species at Dartmouth (Reading, 1862).

Two adults were seen at Gara Rock in 1961 by C.H. Wells (Anon., 1962). First and second-brood adults were seen in two localities in 1990 (M. Catt).

Reading (1862) recorded the Small Blue at Plymouth. This may have been in the old railway cutting at Stoke where it was seen by K. Tucker in 1980. This site has now been bulldozed and built over.

The Small Blue was known on Braunton Burrows before 1986 (Harding, 1986), but the first detailed records were by S.D. Bruce and M. and B. Blackmore in 1988 - both the spring and summer broods were seen, and in 1989. Also in 1988, the Small Blue was noted on Northam Burrows for the first time (information from K. Bastow).

Unconfirmed sightings by P. & M. Sherratt on the old railway [SS4730] near Instow on Aug. 8th 1987 may be genuine, as there have been sightings near Fremington Creek [SS4932] on Aug. 15th 1989 by B. Price, and at Yelland [SS5133] on the old railway in July 1988 and Aug. 10th 1989 by R.J. Darwen. There were also sightings at Kipling Torr and Appledore in July and August 1989 (B. Price).

Inland, there have been sighting at Orley Common, Ipplepen in 1979, 1984 and 1985 by K. Bastow, and the early 1980s by R. Khan, but not since, despite searches for larvae, ova and adults in 1988 and 1989 by K. Bastow and D. Smallshire. This now seems an unlikely habitat for the Small Blue, as the larval foodplant, Kidney Vetch, no longer grows there, although it was growing there in the early 1980s (R. Khan). In 1986, it was reported to K. Bastow that the Small Blue had been found at Stoneycombe, Kingskerswell. In 1989, one was caught on July 23rd by P. Butter, who reports that Kidney Vetch grows in what appears to be a good habitat for the Small Blue. There are reputed sightings near Bovey Tracey [SX8379] in 1986, and along the Bugford Valley from 1974 to 1979 [SS6042].

**Life history**

The Small Blue is generally a spring butterfly, although there is often a late summer second brood. The first brood usually occurs from late May until about the third week in June (earliest and latest dates are May 12th (in 1971, K.M. White) and July 5th (in 1987, K. Tucker)), and the second brood in August (earliest date July 27th (in 1984, S.E. Moore, and 1992, M. Edwards), and the latest, September 14th (in 1986, K. Tucker, N. Ward and J. Johnson)).

The larval foodplant, Kidney Vetch *Anthyllis vulneraria*, is widespread in Devon, but confined mostly to coastal sites (Ivimey-Cook, 1984), with only a few inland records.

Thomas and Webb (1984) note that in Dorset, an average-sized colony consists of 20-30 adults living on a few Kidney Vetch plants. Because of the small size of the colonies, and the fact that adults rarely fly far, sites are especially vulnerable to changing, quite local, conditions. For example, heavy grazing can remove all the Kidney Vetch flower heads with disastrous results for the Small Blue.

Eggs are laid on flower heads of Kidney Vetch. On hatching, the larva eats into the flower and feeds on the developing seed. The species overwinters as a pupa in a crevice in the ground.

## Short-tailed Blue *Everes argiades* (Pallas)

A Short-tailed Blue was recorded on the bank of the River Dart in 1986 (Cole, 1986, p. 20). Mr B. Harley (*pers. commn.*) saw a film of the specimen in question - it turned out to be a Purple Hairstreak.

## Silver-studded Blue *Plebejus argus* (Linnaeus)                Plate 11a

During the nineteenth century, the Silver-studded Blue was known from only six localities in Devon: Torquay, Teignmouth, Bovey Tracey, Axminster (Reading, 1862), Pinhay cliffs and Bolt Head (Parfitt, 1878). However, during the early part of the twentieth century, it was recorded at several more sites (Longstaff, 1907b; Wright, 1932 and Palmer, 1946). Records of the Devonshire Association, both published (Stidston, 1952) and unpublished, principally for the period 1930-1960, data supplied by the BRC, Monks Wood (mainly for 1960-1970), and information gathered during the Devon Butterfly Mapping Scheme (mostly for the 1980s), has increased the number of sites where the Silver-studded Blue has been observed to 55. However, there are only 15 tetrads (concentrated on the East Devon heathlands) where the species currently breeds. In some cases, e.g Torquay, Plymouth, Braunton etc., colonies have become extinct, at other localities, such as Hole and Horrabridge, there is no evidence that colonies were established, and the specimens may have been strays, although Thomas and Webb (1984) and Read (1986) note that adults never wander far from their self-contained colonies.

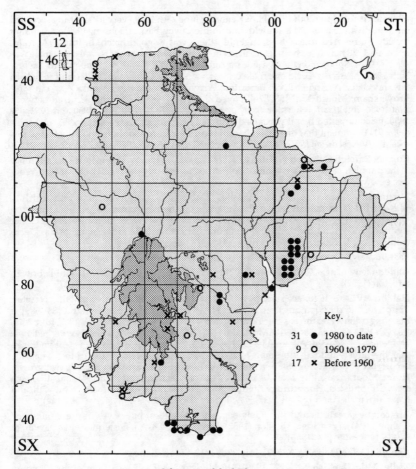

Silver-studded Blue

Below, in alphabetical order, is a resumé of all the localities from which the Silver-studded Blue has been recorded:

**Axminster**. Reading (1862). **Aylesbeare and Harpford Commons** [SY0690], a breeding colony.

**Bicton Common** [SY0486], a breeding colony. **Blackdown Hills** [ST1414], Read (1986). **Bolberry** *[SX6838]*, F.W. Jeffery, July 15th 1973; Read (1986); 1989, M. Catt. **Bolt Head, Salcombe** *[SX7236]*, Bignell (Parfitt, 1878) 'abundant'. Not seen again until 1936 (BRC, Monks Wood). Subsequent sightings are June 27th 1952, D.W. Mitchell, July 23rd 1955 when it was 'common', S.T. Stidston, and July 2nd 1963, H.G. Hurrell. P. Jeffery (*pers. commn.*) informs us that between 1950 and the early 70s, it used to be common between Start Point and Bolt Tail. One male on June 27th, two males and one female on June 28th 1988, M. Hazell; adults July 9th 1988, K. Goatly; and June 22nd 1992, M. Hazell. **Bovey Tracey** - see Bovey Heath. **Bovey Heath**. A breeding colony which has probably declined considerably in the last twenty years as a result of habitat destruction. This is probably the Bovey Tracey locality of Reading (1862). There is no subsequent record until July 14th 1898 (HEC - ex-colln. Hamm), and then a further gap in the record to 1924 when it was 'locally abundant', E.D. Morgan. Subsequent records include 'abundant in some years' (Doe, 1938); 'common, but local, for the period 1948-1951', A.H. Dobson; 'very common and flying just after sunrise' on June 20th 1961, H.A. Kennard; June 28th 1969, 'very local', being recorded on the railway banks at Heathfield, and in the Bovey Basin (Dobson, 1969) - this latter locality he referred to as 'its stronghold'; there was a 'good hatch' in July 1970, G.M. Spooner. 1970 may have been its nadir, as there are few subsequent records; one male was seen by G.M. Spooner on the east side on August 4th 1981. It was 'quite numerous' on July 20th 1986, A. Archer-Lock; one male on July 12th 1988, and several males and females a few days later, A. Archer-Lock. **Braunton**, Wright (1932) and BRC, Monks Wood in 1967. **Brownsham, Mouth Mill** [SS2826]. Noted by Read (1986) as having occurred between 1960-1980. **Buckfastleigh Moor**. Stidston observed *argus* here in 1946, 1950 and 1952. For 1950, he commented that it was a bad year; only two males were seen in 1952. Dobson's (1969:911) comment that there is no recent record for Dartmoor presumably refers to this locality. **Burlescombe** *[ST0816]*, F.H. Lyon, 1952 (Dev. Ass.); 1979, BRC, Monks Wood.

**Colaton Raleigh Common** [SY0486 to 0487], a breeding colony. **Culmstock** - the reference in the Blundell's School Magazine to 'Culmstock' is probably the Maiden Down occurrence (see below).

**Dartmouth**. There are specimens labelled 'Dartmouth', caught on June 16th and July 14th-23rd 1898, in the HEC (ex-colln. Sidgwick). **Dawlish Warren** [SX9878], a singleton was seen on Aug. 29th 1981 by W.A. Ely, presumably a stray, as there has been no other sighting. There are however, earlier sightings at Ladies Mile to the south (q.v.). **Dean-combe, Buckfastleigh** [SX7264], August 1972, R. Baker (Dev. Ass.).

**East Budleigh Common** [SY0484], a breeding colony.

**Gaddon Down, near Cullompton** [ST0711], 1908 (BRC, Monks Wood). **Gallant le Bower**, Stidston (1952).

**Haldon**. 1929 to 1940; seen again in 1991 by M.R. Hughes. **Harpford Hill, Newton Poppleford** [SY0689], a breeding colony. **Hawkerland Valley, Hawkerland** [SY0589], a breeding colony. **Heathfield** - see Bovey Heath. **Hennock (Reservoirs)** *[SX8082]*, June 26th, July 7th 1956, C.W. Holcroft (RAMM). **Hole** [SS4703], July 3rd 1974, a freshly emerged male and female, T. Jenkyn. A search in 1989 by K. Bastow was unsuccessful. T. Jenkyn thinks that the Silver-studded Blue may have used the old railway as a corridor - note the occurrence at Horrabridge Station in 1937. The line of the railway is now badly overgrown. **Holne Moor (near)**, July 22nd 1898, HEC (ex-colln. Hamm); July 7th 1948 and June 30th 1953, S.T. Stidston. **Horrabridge Station** [SX5069], the origin of one male on July 7th, and two worn males on July 24th 1937, F.W. Jeffery (Doe, 1938) is a mystery (see Hole).

**Ilfracombe (area)**. 'Found in widely separated localities, but never in great numbers' (Palmer, 1941). **Ivybridge**, Stidston (1952); June 22nd 1988, A.J. Easterman, on a pavement east of Ivybridge [SX6456].

**Kenton (Oxton House)** [SX9282], July 28th 1913, Studd diaries.

**Ladies Mile, Dawlish** *[SX9777]*, 1929-1940, H. Henstock (Dev. Ass.). **Lympstone Common** [SY0284], a breeding colony.

**Maiden Down, Culmstock** *[ST0815]*, June 9th 1949 (Blundell's School Mag.); July 12th 1970, when it was said to be common, G.M. Spooner; 1974-76, 1978, 1980 and 1981, R.D. Sutton; and 1984 G.M. Spooner. **Membland Drive, Noss Mayo** [SX5246], Aug. 1st 1952, singleton, P. Jeffery (see Noss Mayo). **Mortehoe**, July 3rd 1906 'Common' [in the parish of Mortehoe] among *Erica cinerea* (Longstaff, 1907b) (specimens in HEC dated July 2nd 1906); Aug. 23rd 1968 (BRC, Monks Wood). **Mutters Moor, Sidmouth** [SY1088], 1966, T.J. Richards (BRC, RAMM).

**New Bridge, Holne** [SX7170], June 1948, O.G. Watkins. **Newton Abbot (Milber Down)**, August 1908, 1926, E.D. Morgan; 1949, 'a very small colony', A.H. Dobson. **Noss Mayo** [SX5347], July 1969 (BRC, Monks Wood). See also Membland Drive.

**Paignton (Paignton Reservoir)**, July 12th 1935, S.T. Stidston. **Pinhay cliffs**, Morris (1876). **Plymouth**. 'Rare', F.W. Jeffery (Heath, 1946). **Putsborough** *[SS4440]*, 'fairly common', June 24th 1933 (Doe, 1941).

**Rackenford Moor** [SS8521], an existing colony.

**Soar Mill Cove** *[SX6937]*, July 8th 1963, two or three specimens, H.G. Hurrell. There is a post-1980 record on Read's (1986) map for both this locality, and the tetrad to the north. **Soar Mill Cove** [SX6937] to **Start Point** [SX8237], nine loose colonies, 1990 to 1992, M. Catt. **Start Point** [SX8137], June 29th 1964, BRC, Monks Wood; July 1984, P.A. Good; July 1st 1984, T.D. Sleep; June 15th 1971, F.W. Jeffery between Start and Prawle Points. **Stover**, Aug. 6th 1960, F.W. Jeffery.

Teignmouth (Parfitt, 1878). **Torquay**. (Reading 1862). **Torquay (Watcombe)**. Aug. 11th 1908 'Local' (Walker, 1930); possibly the Torquay locality of Reading (1862).

**Venn Ottery Common** [SY0691], a breeding colony.

**Wembury** *[SX5248]*, E.W. Clarke (Heath, 1946). **Woodbury**. A breeding colony, for which, surprisingly, the first record was not until June 26th 1912, F. Blanchard (specimen in RAMM). Woodbury is probably just a general locality and probably includes Lympstone, East Budleigh, Bicton and Colaton Raleigh commons. **Woolacombe**, singleton, July 1902 (Longstaff, 1907b).

**Yarner Wood** [SX7778], early 1960s (BRC, Monks Wood).

The Silver-studded Blue generally flies from the second week of July until the middle of August. Earliest and latest dates are May 28th 1990 (M. Catt) and August 29th 1981 (W.A. Ely).

Adults have a very short life span - an average of 3 days for males, 3.4 days for females, although longer spans occur (17 days for a female, 25 days for a male) (Read, 1986).

Colonies are generally closed, and from which individuals rarely move. Read (1986) showed that a patch of scrub no more than 2m high or 4m wide acts as a barrier to dispersal. The size of a colony may be less than half a hectare, in which densities vary from ten or less in a colony facing imminent extinction, to many thousands. The distribution of the Silver-studded Blue is not limited by the larval foodplant, since it feeds on a widely distributed variety - including *Erica cinerea, E. tetralix, Calluna vulgaris* and *Ulex gallii* (Read, 1986). According to Read, the optimum habitat requirement for the Silver-studded Blue is a warm, sheltered, lowland heathland in the 'building' phase of its succession. To maintain the optimum phase, Read recommends that approximately one sixteenth, depending on local conditions, of an area should be cut, burnt or grazed each year. Because of the fragmented state of much of Devon's heathland, isolated colonies of the Silver-studded Blue are more likely to become extinct, and, as a result of its sedentary nature, recolonisation is unlikely, even though the habitat may be suitable. Because of its lack of mobility, Read recommends that consideration should be given to its reintroduction to habitats that have, or can be, returned to conditions suitable for successful breeding.

## Brown Argus *Aricia agestis* ([D&S])                    Plate 10f

Both Parfitt's (1878) description of the Brown Argus as 'Generally distributed, but it cannot be called common', and Stidston's (1952) comment that the Brown Argus is 'not at all common, but widely distributed', are still true today.

The larval foodplants are Rock Rose *Helianthemum chamaecistus* and Common Stork's-bill *Erodium cicutarium*. From the distribution of the above plants (Ivimey-Cook, 1984), compared to the distribution of the Brown Argus, it appears that in Devon, the Common Stork's-bill is the main foodplant. Possibly, as in Cornwall (Henwood, 1990), the Smooth Crane's-bill *Geranium molle* is also utilised.

61

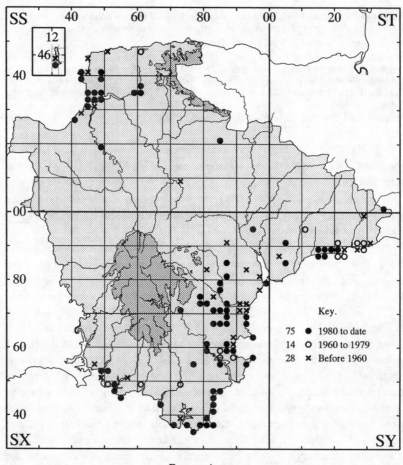

Brown Argus

In both sexes, the Brown Argus resembles the female Common Blue, but it is smaller (29mm, as opposed to 33mm), a deep chocolate-brown without any blue scaling, and with a prominent row of orange spots on the hindwing margin. It is double brooded: a spring brood from mid-May (May 3rd 1982, S.D. Bruce) to the end of June; and a summer brood in August (to Oct. 11th in 1989, S.D. Bruce).

When the butterfly mapping scheme started in 1985, it looked as though the Brown Argus had contracted its range over the last thirty years, even though it was recorded from several tetrads where it had not been seen before (Bristow and Bolton, 1986, fig. 38). Since that time, it has been found on an additional thirty tetrads, on some of which (i.e. Torquay, SX9464) it had not been recorded since the beginning of the century. Unfortunately, the way that the data are presented in the accompanying map does not differentiate between spots which represent long-established colonies, new sightings at old colonies, and apparently new colonies.

The following is an alphabetical list of all localities at which the Brown Argus has been recorded:

**Abbotsham Cliffs** [SS4127], Aug. 19th 1989, D. Churchill. **Axminster**, Reading (1862). **Axmouth (Springhead)** [SY2790], J.R.W. Coxhead, 1975, 1976 (Wallace, 1979). **Axmouth-Lyme Regis cliffs**, 1956, T.J. Wallace (Wallace, 1979); 1960+ (BRC, Monks Wood). **Aylesbeare Common** [SY0590], July 24th 1987, D. Tye.

**Baggy Point, Croyde** [SS4240], Sept. 4th 1986, E. Towns. **Bantham, near Kingsbridge** [SX6643], Aug. 7th 1983, E. Hart. **Beesands** [SX8240], 1989, M. Catt. **Berry Head, Brixham** [SX9456], c.1924, E.D. Morgan; June 15th 1986 and July 1986, K. Tucker, N. Ward and J. Johnson; 1989, M. Catt. **Bickington (near A38)** [SX7972], July 13th 1986, K. Bastow; May 20th 1990, S.H. Mitchell. **Bishopsteignton**, C.W. Holcroft, Sept. 1st 1954 (RAMM). **Blackpool** [SX8173], May 12th 1990, S.H. Mitchell. **Boreston**, pre-1950, F.W. Jeffery. **Bovey Valley Woodlands** [SX7879], 1984, D.J. Land. **Branscombe (Berry Cliff)** [SY1988], 1975, J.R.W. Coxhead (Wallace, 1979); Aug. 5th 1984, I.D. Page. **Branscombe-Beer Head**, breeding colonies. **Braunton** [SS4835], June 20th 1986; Aug. 2nd 1989, S.D. Bruce. **Braunton Burrows**. A breeding colony. **Brixham (Sharkham Point)** *[SX9354]*, 1951, A.H. Dobson (Dev. Ass.); 1989, M. Catt. **Budleigh Salterton**, 1903 (HEC - ex-colln. Meldola).

**Chelfham, near Barnstaple** [SS6035], 1990, J. Butter. **Chudleigh Knighton Heath** [SX8477], 1984, D.J. Hopkins. **Paignton (Clennon Valley)** [SX8859], Aug. 14th 1982, S.D. Buckthorpe. Site since ploughed up and reseeded. **Combe Martin** [SS6046], 1978 (BRC, Monks Wood). **Cunnilear Wood** [SS6136], 1984, Q. Paynter.

**Dartmoor**, Aug. 23rd 1823, Dr Leach (var. *ataxerces*) (Parfitt, 1878). **Dawlish**, (Barrett, 1906). **Dawlish Warren** [SX9878], 1989, M. Catt. **Dittisham Mill Creek, Dittisham** [SX8555], Aug. 13th 1985, B.A. Baker.

**East Budleigh Common** [SY0484], Aug. 8th 1986, D.A. Gee. **East Prawle** *[SX7836]*, Aug. 20th 1967 (Dev. Ass.). **Exeter**, Reading (1862); Barrett (1906). **Exeter (Beacon Heath)** [SX9495], July 31st 1984, R.J. Clarke. **Exeter (Pinhoe)** [SX9595], 1970s; [SX9494], 1980s, R.J. Clarke.

**Finlake, Chudleigh** [SX8479], July 16th 1989, D. Smallshire. **Fordlands** *[SX8690]*, June 21st 1919 (RAMM).

**Galmpton Quarry, Galmpton** [SX8856], June 5th 1965, C. Longworth-Dames. **Gara Point - Stoke Point, Noss Mayo** [SX5246 - 5646], 1981, E.C.M. Haes. (See also Membland Drive). **Gara Rock, Salcombe** [SX7436], 1989, M. Catt. **Goodrington** [SX8858], June 6th, Aug. 19th and 31st, Sept. 9th 1986, S.D. Buckthorpe.

**Hakeford** [SS6134], Aug. 6th 1990, D. Smallshire. **Haldon** [SX8784], Aug. 12th and 17th 1987, D. Smallshire. **Haldon (Kiddens Plantation)** [SX8784], a breeding colony. **Hallsands** [SX8038], 1989, M. Catt. **Harbertonford** [SX7755], June 18th 1988, A.R. Hawtin - one only, pupa possibly brought in with topsoil. **Hares Down** [SS8521], 1983, P.F. Allfrey. **Hatherleigh** [SS5404], Aug. 21st 1985, J. Pitman (unconfirmed). **Hawkchurch** [ST3000], K.A. Gosling, first seen (a female) on May 24th 1980; 1984; May 29th 1985. **Hennock (Reservoirs)** *[SX8082]*, C.W. Holcroft, 1953 (RAMM). **Horsey Island** [SS4735], June 20th 1986, S.D. Bruce; Aug. 9th 1986 and Aug. 4th 1987, M. & B. Blackmore.

**Ilfracombe (area)** (Palmer, 1946). **Instow**, pre-1950, F.W. Jeffery.

**Kenton (Oxton)** *[SX9282]*, July 21st 1899, Studd Collection (RAMM). **Kingskerswell**, 1924, E.D. Morgan (common) (Dev. Ass.). **Knowle** [SS4838], June 17th 1989, T.D. & J. Sleep.

**Labrador Bay** [SX9369], May 13th 1990, S.H. Mitchell. **Lannacombe Cliff** [SX8036], 1989, M. Catt. **Lapford**, Aug. 15th 1926 (RAMM). **Liverton (Rora Wood)** [SX7975], July 21st 1990, S.H. Mitchell. **Loddiswell** [SX7348], 1966 (BRC, Monks Wood). **Lundy**, Heaven (Chanter, 1877); Longstaff (1907a). Said to be extinct by 1947 (Sherwood, 1975), but seen again on July 27th 1989, A.M. Jewels.

**Membland Drive, Noss Mayo** [SX5346], Aug. 2nd 1961, F.W. Jeffery. A nearby colony existed from at least 1947 - c.1973. E.C.M. Haes. (See also Gara Point - Stoke Point). **Mortehoe district**, 1932-45, R.J. Burton (Dev. Ass.).

Newton Abbot (Aller Park Brake) [SX8769], R. Woods, 1975-79 (BRC, RAMM); Newton Abbot (Bradley Wood), July 24th 1898 (HEC - ex-colln. Hamm); Newton Abbot (Bradley Manor) [SX8470], July 22nd 1984 and Aug. 23rd 1986, S.D. Buckthorpe; Newton Abbot (Decoy) [SX8670], Aug. 1976 and Aug. 31st 1987, S.H. Mitchell; Newton Abbot (Decoy Wood) [SX8670], July 15th 1989. S.H. Mitchell; Newton Abbot (Milber Down), J. Walker, 1908 (Dev. Ass.); Newton Abbot (Ogwell Mill Lane) [SX8470], July and August 1991, S.H. Mitchell; Newton Abbot (Rackerhayes) [SX8672], Sept. 9th 1987, S.H. Mitchell. Northam Burrows [SS4430], Aug. 26th 1980, K.C. Tyson; Aug. 15th 1986, E. Towns. Noss Mayo (The Warren) [SX5346], June 4th 1988, E.C.M. Haes; 1989, M. Catt.

Orley Common, Ipplepen [SX8266], May 30th 1985, D. Overy; June 1987, K. Bastow. Ottery St Mary [SY1095], 1972 (BRC, Monks Wood).

Paignton, Aug. 5-7th 1913 (HEC, ex-colln Woodforde), 1916, May 1917, 1921, P.P. Milman (Dev. Ass.). Paignton (Kings Ash) [SX8661], May 24th 1989, A.R. Hawtin. Paignton (Preston Down) [SX8862], June 26th 1952 (Dev. Ass.). Paignton (Yalberton) [SX8659], June 11th, July 26th and Aug. 4th 1987, A.R. Hawtin. Pinhay cliffs, (Morris, 1876). Plymouth (Turnchapel, and Bovisand), Reading (1862); Barrett (1906); c.1924, E.D. Morgan (Dev. Ass.). Plymouth (Jennycliff, Hooe) [SX4952], Aug. 14th 1983, E. Hart (singleton). Plymouth (Breakwater Road, Pomphlett) [SX5053], Aug. 15th 1983, E. Hart (singleton). Prawle Point [SX7735], 1989; 1990, M. Catt. Prawle Wood [SX7936], Aug. 25th 1985, D.J. Hopkins. Putsborough, August 1932 (Ilfracombe Museum).

Rackenford Moor [SS8521], 1983, P.F. Allfrey. Ranscombe [SX8681], July 14th 1990, D. Smallshire. River Dart Country Park, Ashburton [SX7370], C.R. Bristow, Aug. 7th 1983. Riversmead [SS5935], Aug. 9th 1990, J. Butter. Rousdon Landslip [SY2888], 1957-59 (Dev. Ass); 1960+ (BRC, Monks Wood); The Plateau [SY2989], June 1956, A.G. Tomlinson (Wallace, 1967); Goat Island [SY2789], 1957, May 30th, T.W. Turner (Wallace, 1967).

Salcombe (Barrett, 1906); The Warren [SX7136], 1990, M. Catt. Salcombe (Sharp Tor) [SX7236], 1990, M. Catt. Saunton (Saunton Headland) [SS4338], June 4th 1985, S.D. Bruce. Shaldon (Shaldon Cliffs) [SX9371], C.W. Holcroft, Aug. 26th 1953 (RAMM). Slapton [SX8244], 1989, M. Catt. Slapton Ley [SX8242], Aug. 30th 1962 (Dev. Ass.); 1989, M. Catt. Soar Mill Cove [SX6937], 1990, M. Catt. Southleigh [SY2091], B. Henwood (BRC, RAMM). Southleigh (near Bovey Down) [SY2790], 1975 and 1976, B. Henwood. Southway [SX6148], post-1960 (BRC, Plymouth). Spreacombe [SS4841], June 11th 1987; Aug. 18th 1989, M. & B. Blackmore. Springhead [SY2790], 1975 and 1976, J.R.W. Coxhead (Wallace, 1979). Starcross (Barrett, 1906). Start Point (west of) [SX8237], June 15th 1988, M. Pool; 1989, 1990, M. Catt. Stoke Gabriel [SX8558 and 8557], 1966 (BRC, Monks Wood). Stokeinteignhead, 1924, E.D. Morgan (Dev. Ass.). Stoneycombe (Kerswell Down Hill) [SX8667], July 23rd 1989, P. Butter. Stoneycombe (Miltor Mator Common) [SX8567], Aug. 17th 1985, D. Munden; [SX8566], May 21st 1988, S.H. Mitchell. Stover Woods, C.W. Holcroft, Aug. 21st 1956 (RAMM). Strete [SX82-8446], 1989, M. Catt.

Teignmouth, Reading (1862); Barrett (1906). Totnes [SX8060], July 31st 1976, D.W. Mitchell (Dev. Ass.). Totnes (Brutus Bridge), May 28th 1987, A.R. Hawtin. Totnes (Lake Gardens) [SX8059], 1980 (BRC, Monks Wood). Torquay (Hope's Nose) [SX9463], 1908, J. Walker; 1936, H. Henstock (Dev. Ass.); July 4th 1989, S.E. Moore. Torquay (Maidencombe) [SX9268], 1951, A.H. Dobson (Dev. Ass.). Torquay (Valley of Rocks, Watcombe) [SX9267], May 26th 1990, S.H. Mitchell.

Wembury Point [SX5048], Aug. 5th 1969, A.P. Gainsford (Dev. Ass.). Weston Coombe, Weston, 1990, M.S. Warren. Westward Ho!, pre-1950, F.W. Jeffery. Woolacombe, May 22nd 1905 (HEC). Woodbury, 1933-40, H. Henstock (Dev. Ass.).

Yealmpton [SX5650], pre-1950, F.W. Jeffery. Yelland [SS4832], May 27th 1989, D. Churchill. Youlston Wood, near Barnstaple [SS6036], 1984, Q. Paynter.

---

# Common Blue *Polyommatus icarus* (Rottemburg)     Plate 11b

The Common Blue is widely distributed and can usually be found in small numbers on rough ground wherever its foodplants (Common and Marsh Birdsfoot-trefoil *Lotus corniculatus* and *L. uliginosus*, Lesser Yellow Trefoil *Trefoil dubium*, Common Restharrow *Ononis repens*, Spiny Restharrow *O. spinosa*, and Clovers *Trifolium* spp.) occur. The general patchy mapped distribution

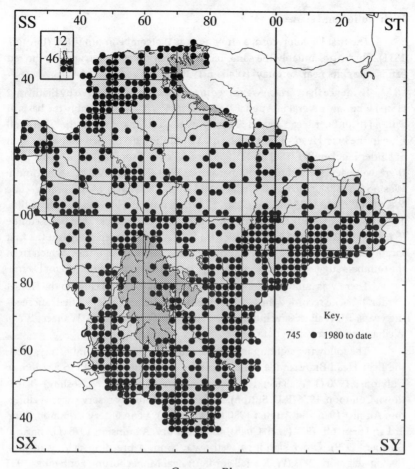

Common Blue

across central Devon is probably partly explained by recording bias. It should occur on many of the areas of unimproved grassland across this central tract.

The Common Blue is double brooded, with the spring brood flying from June (occasionally late May, exceptionally in April - April 1st, 1957 (F.W. Jeffrey), and the second brood from late July through into September or even October (Oct. 8th, T.D. Sleep).

## Chalk-hill Blue *Lysandra coridon* (Poda)                Plater 11c

The Chalk-hill Blue used to, or perhaps does intermittently, breed on areas of coastal chalk in East Devon, where it was last seen in 1981 (M.S. Warren). In addition to the former breeding colonies in East Devon, there have been several sightings of strays scattered throughout Devon.

## Distribution and status

The first Devon record, a stray, was at Watcombe in June 1899 (Lupton, 1911). This is presumably the same record as 'one taken by a friend on the red sandstone cliffs near Torquay' (Walker, 1930).

Evidence that *coridon* was breeding in the county was given by Blathwayt (1909) who saw several in August 1908 and 1909. This was probably the basis of Tutt's (1910) Beer Head record. There was no further record of the Chalk-hill Blue in the Beer Head - Branscombe area until the 1960's when they were seen at Under Hooken [SY2188] up to 1968 by S. Glover. From that time, up to 1981, there were several sightings: Branscombe, 1970 (R. Wakely), Weston Mouth, Weston [SY1688], *c*.1970 (T.J. Wallace) and Aug. 7th 1976 (A. Mort); Branscombe West [SY1988] in 1973 and Aug. 28th 1978 (one only, B. Henwood); Berry Cliffs, 1975 (J.R.W. Coxhead); Beer Undercliff, 1976 (A. Archer-Lock), and Branscombe [SY2088 and 2188] on Aug. 18th 1981 (M.S. Warren). Warren saw 10 at the first locality in half an hour, and one at the second. Warren's sightings, which from the numbers suggest that these were more than just strays, are the last for Devon.

There was another colony at Whitland Cliff [SY3090] close to the Dorset border. J. Locke recorded the Chalk-hill Blue in 1973 and [unspecified] succeeding years; T.J. Wallace saw more than 20 there on Sept. 4th 1978 (Wallace, 1979). We have no more recent data.

The following sighting in East Devon were almost certainly strays from the Beer Head-Branscombe area: Salcombe Hill, Aug. 4th 1949 (S.E. Moore); Colyton, *c*.1970 (T. Wallace); Hawkchurch, August 1973 (K.A. Gosling); Blackdown Common, 1976 (R.D. Sutton); Little Breach Butterfly reserve near Wellington, August 1976 and August 1980 (R.D. Sutton); Venn Ottery Common, Aug. 3rd and Sept. 6th 1977 (G.H. Gush), and Musbury, Axminster, 1978 (I.B. Barton) (Turner, 1979). Other sightings well away from a breeding colony include Bishopsteignton, 1903 (W. R. Hall-Jordan); Zeal Monachorum, September 1935 (Studd Colln.); North Tawton, Aug. 1943 (O.G. Watkins) and Huntshaw, Aug. 1947 (G.H. Gush).

The larvae of the Chalk-hill Blue feed on Horseshoe Vetch *Hippocrepis comosa*. On the East Devon sites where *coridon* has been found, this occurs on south-facing cliffs and broken ground. In Devon, the adults have been found throughout August, and into early September. In Dorset, the nearest colonies of which are about 20km inside the county boundary, they can be found from July onwards (Thomas and Webb, 1984, p. 69).

---

## Adonis Blue *Lysandra bellargus* (Rottemburg)　　　　　Plate 11d

The Adonis Blue is extinct in East Devon, having been last seen in 1978, but survives at a very low density in the Torbay area.

*L. bellargus* is a very local species restricted to one larval foodplant, the Horseshoe Vetch *Hippocrepis comosa*, which grows on unimproved limestone and chalk soils. In Devon, the Horseshoe Vetch is confined to a few coastal sites near Branscombe and Torquay (Ivimey-Cook, 1984). Consequently, any record away from the known foodplant localities, or areas on non-calcareous soils where the foodplant is unlikely to occur, is suspect.

The earliest reference to the Adonis Blue in Devon was by Stainton (1857) at Torquay. Reading (1862) added detail to this locality by noting that it occurred at Chapel Hill and Anstey's Cove, as well as at Seaton and Sidmouth in the east of the county. A third locality at Torquay, Hope's Nose, was added by W.B. (Dev. Ass.) who recorded that on August 13th, 1866, the species was abundant. Parfitt (1878) repeated the earlier records of Chapel Hill, Anstey's Cove and Hope's Nose, but made no comment on the status of the species. However, by the turn of the century, the Adonis Blue began to decline. Barrett (1906) noted that it was 'formerly locally common'. In 1908 it was recorded from Meadfoot, Watcombe and Chapel Hill by Walker (Dev. Ass.). In 1909, it was still described as abundant, but local (no specific locality given) at Torquay (Lupton, 1911). Walker (1933) recorded that the Adonis Blue first disappeared from Chapel Hill, then from Hope's Nose, lingering on at Anstey's Cove until about 1910. According to Walker (1933), it died out at its fourth locality, Daddyhole Plain, Meadfoot, in 1931, but Dobson (1969) stated that it survived there until 1943. Walker (1930; 1933) could offer no explanation for the decline of the colonies; it was not due to overcollecting, the habitat appeared not to have changed, and the foodplant was plentiful. He tried twice, in 1911 and 1912, to re-establish the Adonis Blue, by liberating Kentish stock at Anstey's Cove, but the attempts were unsuccessful.

A small colony still exists in the Torbay area. Singletons were seen in September 1973 (I. Rippey), June 1982, 1983 and 1985 (N. Smallbones) and June 1989 (S.E. Moore).

Torbay was one of the most westerly localities for the species in Britain, although Goss (1877, p. 96) refers to 'adonis' as being common in an area near Plymouth on June 28th 1876. The larval foodplant has not been recorded from the Plymouth area (Ivimey-Cook, 1984).

Whereas the Torquay occurrences were fairly well known, the East Devon localities for the Adonis Blue received little attention, which is surprising, since the species survived there up to 1978.

Reading's (1862) record of the Adonis Blue at Seaton and Sidmouth was repeated by Newman (1869) and Parfitt (1878). Majendie (1891) described it as fairly plentiful near Sidmouth in 1889. In the Studd diaries, there is an entry for the capture of an Adonis Blue at Sidmouth on Aug. 11th 1896. Wells (1897) recorded it as abundant on the cliffs at Sidmouth.

The above occurrences were presumably a separate colony to that noted by Blathwayt (1909, pp. 212, 323) as '2.5 miles west of Beer Head' in 1908 and Aug. 13th 1909. It was described as a 'flourishing colony' in 1909. On June 6th 1930, the Adonis Blue was 'abundant' (together with 26 other species of butter-flies!) (Demuth, 1985, p. 13). The spring brood was also observed by T. Jenkyn on May 25th 1934 when he captured 1 male and 6 females. Stidston (1952) wrote that there were no recent captures of *bellargus* from Sidmouth, Beer and Seaton.

However, Carr (1955) saw the species at Branscombe on Aug. 10th 1955. There is then a gap in the records until the 1970s. A.H.J. Smart noted it at Under Hooken up to 1971. The last locality at which Adonis Blue were recorded is at Branscombe West Cliff, where it was seen by S. Glover in 1973 (Glover, 1987, p. 3) and by B. Henwood in 1973, 1975, 1976 and 1978. Henwood (*pers. commn.*) believes that it was the change in habitat since the 1930s that caused such a terrific decline for both *bellargus* and *coridon* (see also Demuth, 1985). The severe drought of 1976 was probably the final blow. On June 19th 1978, Henwood found some ova of *bellargus* on *Hippocrepis comosa*, and on August 28th 1978 he saw one adult. This appears to have been the last record of the Adonis Blue in East Devon. A search by Glover in 1983 was fruitless (Glover, 1987, p. 3). Tyson, visiting the area in mid-August 1987 (Tyson, 1987a, p. 4), saw no Adonis Blue (nor Chalk-hill Blue, the reason for his visit) along the coastal path [SY1788 to 2188] on Aug. 12th and Sept. 2nd 1989. Similarly, searches [SY2188] by D. Tye on June 17th 1988 and May 29th 1989 found neither the larval foodplant nor the adult.

There appears to have been a third colony farther east. G.M. Spooner found the species at the Landslip Nature Reserve [SY2888] in August 1924. It was seen at Springhead [SY2790] by J.R.W. Coxhead on June 14th 1975.

Now, the nearest colonies of the Adonis Blue are about 20km away, inside Dorset (Thomas and Webb, 1984, p. 71).

## Green-underside Blue *Glaucopsyche alexis* (Poda)      Plate 10e

A male of this common European species was caught at Torquay in September 1936 by C. Down (Howarth, 1973). It is now in the Natural History Museum, London.

## Holly Blue *Celastrina argiolus* (Linnaeus)      Plate 11e

This is a widespread species that probably occurs in most areas where the larval foodplants, Holly *Ilex aquifolium* and Ivy *Hedera helix*, occur. Searching for ova and larvae, particularly on Ivy, can be most productive, and can be carried out regardless of the weather. There are two flight periods: in the spring, when it is usually the earliest 'blue' to be seen - generally from late April, occasionally in March (March 9th 1961, F.W. Jeffery) (NB, the Feb. 8th 1990 date in Bowles (1990) is unsubstantiated and should be withdrawn, T.D. Sleep, *pers. commn.*), through May and into June; the second brood flies from late July to September (Oct. 11th 1987, D. Smallshire).

The Holly Blue utilises the Holly in the spring as the larval foodplant, and Ivy for the second generation (i.e those that will emerge in the following spring). The eggs are laid at the base of the unopened flower buds. Other foodplants, such as Dogwood *Swida sanguinea* and Gorse *Ulex europaeus* have been recorded elsewhere in Britain. Second brood Holly Blues were seen egg laying on Heather in Devon in 1989 by K. Orpe (*pers. commn.*). Heather was also

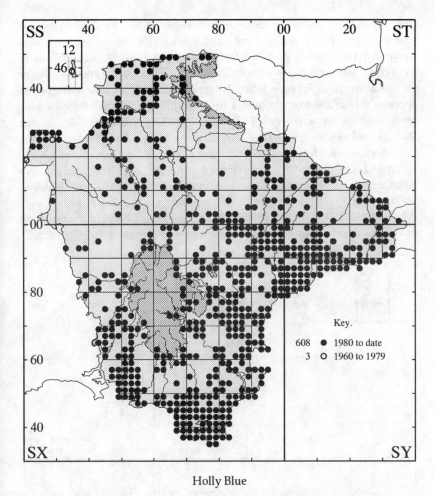

Key.

608 ● 1980 to date
3 ○ 1960 to 1979

Holly Blue

recorded by Asher (1989) as a host plant for second-brood Holly Blues on an East Berkshire heathland and at Silchester on the Berkshire/Hampshire border.

## Large Blue *Maculinea arion eutyphron* (Fruhstorfer)　　Plate 11f

The British race of the Large Blue became extinct in Devon, as well as England, when the last-known colony, on Dartmoor, died out in 1979. Various attempts at conservation of the species, and the reasons for its decline and extinction, are discussed by Spooner (1963), Harvey (1964), Hunt (1964) and Thomas (1980; 1989).

### History and distribution

For most of the nineteenth century, the Large Blue was only known in Devon from the south coast, principally between Bolt Head and Bolt Tail; first recorded by Fairweather (1844). On June 30th 1856, thirteen were taken (Nicholls, 1875; Elliot, 1915). The area was visited again in 1857 and 1859; in this last year '5 dozen were caught'. According to Elliot (1915), the Large Blue was as common as the Meadow Brown in the meadows on the cliff top; in 1859, up to a hundred specimens a day were collected by one person and sold to a dealer for half-a-crown (12.5p) each. Elliot also stated that *arion* could be found on the opposite side of the harbour, under Rickham [SX7337]. Bignell (in Newman, 1869) caught 36 specimens 'near Plymouth' [=Bolt Head (Sheldon, 1929)] in June 1865, as well as taking 'several dozen' in about 1868 at Bolt Head. Gatcombe (1869) took 'several dozen' *c*.1866, and about a fortnight later 'many were taken... by a friend'. On July 7th 1870, about three dozen were caught and '... might have taken more had I desired to do so, but found many of them worn' (Mathew, 1877). About a dozen worn specimens were taken by a collector in July 1875 (Mathew, 1877). On July 15th 1876, Mathew saw one male and four females, all worn, two days later only one specimen was seen (Brown, 1876). Goss (1877),

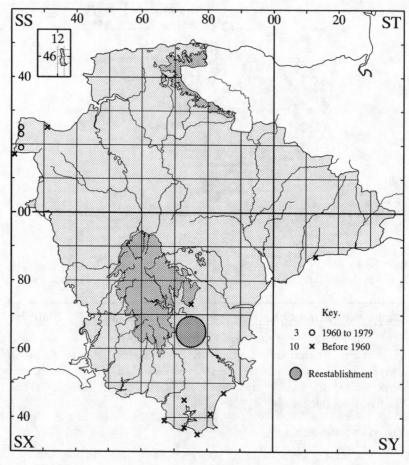

Large Blue

attributed the low numbers and their state to the late time in their flying period, as he caught 28 in three hours on June 26th 1876, and 28 on the following day.

After the 1870s, the Large Blue became scarce (Sheldon, 1923; Nicholls, 1875). Bignell (in Barrett, 1893) believed that it was gorse burning which was responsible for its decline at Bolt Head. None was seen in 1884 (Bignell, 1884), yet by 1890 it was still there and 'about half-a-dozen examples were taken' (Sheldon, 1925). There is one specimen in the HEC dated July 23rd 1890. It was recorded in small scattered colonies between 1892 and 1896 (Prideaux, 1892; Heath, 1946) - a specimen in the HEC from Salcombe is dated July 4th 1892. It was reputedly 'exceedingly scarce' by 1897 (Sheldon, 1925). Harvey (1964) stated that it had virtually disappeared by 1906, but that it was reputed to have been seen in the 1940s. H. Henstock caught a male in 'South Devon' in 1941 (Dev. Ass.). In an undated [c.1947] letter to F.W. Jeffery, Stidston said 'keep it dark about the Salcombe *arion*'. Spooner (1963) hinted that it might have existed at very low density up to at least 1963.

Newman (1869) referred to a secret locality of J.F. Hanbury, 10 miles from Kingsbridge, where it is 'very abundant'. This may be the Little Start, and Beesands, Strete localities of A.B. Farn and R.C. Morgan (Parkinson-Curtis, 1929; Heath, 1946).

The 'Kingsbridge' locality of Jordan (1874) and South (1906) was probably the Bolt Tail to Bolt Head localities, as Kingsbridge was the nearest railhead for those areas. Goss (1877) referred to a locality 'some fifteen miles further west' [of the Bolt Head - Bolt Tail area]. Barrett (1906) stated that it was seen very rarely near Plymouth.

It was reputed to occur at Torquay in the nineteenth century (Ms., Dev. Ass.), and one was recorded near Sidmouth in July 1897 (Heath, 1946).

In 1891, the Large Blue was discovered at Millook on the North Cornwall coast. It was soon found almost continuously between Tintagel and Bude, and in a few localities as far north as Clovelly (Thomas, in Emmet and Heath, 1989). Although the Clovelly site was known before 1880 ('abundant in Dale's day' (South, 1906)), with sporadic records in North Devon during the 1910s and 1930s (Spooner, 1963, p. 200), the North Devon localities did not become widely known until the late 1940s. According to South (1906), the Large Blue was extinct at Clovelly by 1906. Elsewhere in North Devon, numbers increased to a peak in the early 1950s, after favourable seasons in 1949 and 1951 and it could be found in every coombe south of Hartland Quay. Thomas (1989) referred to the marking and release of 800 specimens at Speke's Mill on one day in 1954, and stated that there must have been over 10 000 individuals in that one valley. On July 4th 1958 it was flying in 'fair numbers, even amongst the parked cars', but within a few years it had disappeared from this locality (T. Jenkyn, *pers. commn.*). Also in 1958, on July 3rd, it was 'not uncommon' at St Catherine's Tor (T. Jenkyn, *pers. commn.*). Soon after, a severe decline occurred. In 1963, it could still be found on thirteen sites south of Hartland, but in very low numbers in all but three valleys (Hunt, 1965). H.A. Kennard (Dev. Ass.) stated that '1968 was a very bad year, only several seen'. Mr T. Jenkyn saw one on July 1st 1971 at about 3pm, and another on July 2nd at about 10.15am, with two possible sightings later on. These were the last sightings of the Large Blue in North Devon.

Fairweather (1844) was the first to record the Large Blue at 'Ashburton', presumably on Dartmoor. Parfitt (1878) also recorded that the Large Blue occurred 'near Ashburton'. In July 1936, a colony was found 'on the southern slope of Dartmoor' by J. Walker and S.T. Stidston (Stidston in Doe, 1937; Stidston, 1949; 1950); one was caught. The area was about 12 acres in extent, surrounded on all sides by woods and overgrown hedges. The numbers of adults were always small, but a few were seen each year up to 1946 when two were seen on July 7th (Stidston, 1949). None was seen in 1947; heather completely covered the ground, and was later burnt off (Stidston, 1949).

In 1948, a new locality was sought and found on Dartmoor, and in the following years a few specimens were found - 5 were seen in 1950; 1952 and 1953 were described as good years (Dev. Ass.). When the site was next visited in 1956, it had been ploughed up and no Large Blue was seen

At a third little-known Dartmoor site, the Large Blue persisted to 1979. This was the last colony of *arion* in Britain; the last 15 years are chronicled by Thomas (1980). The site was maintained in a suitable condition, such that the population built up continuously from 1964 to 1973. However, by 1973, the population had increased to beyond the carrying capacity of the site, and severe overcrowding occurred, causing heavy mortality during the immature stages (mainly in the ants nests, as most nests can only support one larva, and in cases of overcrowding, all the larvae die). Adult numbers fell from 300 in 1973 to 100 in 1974. Unfortunately, the colony had no chance to recover, as 1975 and 1976 were years of severe drought. Drought can be harmful to both egg laying, and to the condition of the ants nest. Only about 16 adults emerged in 1977. Of these, less than half (6 or 7) were females, of which one, and possibly two, failed to mate, because the earlier-emerging and short-lived males had already died. In 1978, only two males and three females emerged. These were taken into captivity, but only one female paired. However, 59 larvae were introduced to *M. sabuleti* nests on the site (this was about five times the number produced from females in the wild). In 1979, it looked as though the captive breeding programme had been successful, as 22 adults emerged. These too were taken into captivity, but, unfortunately, they failed to pair, and only a few sterile eggs were laid. Thus, the Large Blue became extinct in Britain.

### Reasons for the decline and extinction

The causes of the decline were discussed by Spooner (1963). Various reasons were put forward as to why the species became extinct at site after site throughout the country.

The first cause examined was that of over collecting. Because of its rarity, and the fact that it cannot readily be bred in captivity, the Large Blue has always been a prized specimen - Baron Bouck had over 770 British specimens in his

J. Breeds

Plate 1a: Braunton Burrows.

S.H. Mitchell.

Plate 1b: Heath Fritillary habitat, Exmoor.

S.H. Mitchell

Plate 2a: Lowland meadows and oak woodland, Bradley Wood.

S.H. Mitchell

Plate 2b: Dartmoor common, managed, Padley Common, Chagford.

Plate 3a: Valley meadow and moorland, Dunsford.

Plate 3b: Ashclyst Forest glade.

S.H. Mitchell

Plate 4a: Grass meadows, Haldon butterfly walk.

S.H. Mitchell

Plate 4b: Recently established embankment, Chudleigh Knighton.

D. Smallshire

Plate 5a: Culm grassland and scrub, Hollow Moor.

S.H. Mitchell

Plate 5b: East Budleigh Common.

S.H. Mitchell

Plate 6a: Small Skipper, female.

RAMM

Plate 6b: Lulworth Skipper, Sidmouth.

RAMM

Plate 6c: Silver-spotted Skipper, female, Exeter, 1907.

D.J. Land

Plate 6d: Large Skipper, Haldon, 1985.

S.H. Mitchell

Plate 6e: Dingy Skipper.

S.H. Mitchell

Plate 6f: Grizzled Skipper.

Plate 7a: Scarce Swallowtail, Woolacombe, 1935.

Plate 7b: Wood White, Haldon, 1984.

Plate 7c: Pale Clouded Yellow, Teignmouth, 1955, C.W. Holcroft.

Plate 7d: Berger's Clouded Yellow, female, N. Devon, 1949.

Plate 7e: Clouded Yellow, female var. *helice*, Haldon, 1983.

Plate 7f: Brimstone, male.

D.J. Land

Plate 8a: Large White, female, Bovey Wood, 1983.

C.R. Bristow

Plate 8b: Small White, 1987.

D.R. Tye

Plate 8c: Green-veined White, Ashclyst, 1991.

BC (Devon Branch)

Plate 8d: Bath White, male, Wembury, 1945.

C.R. Bristow

Plate 8e: Orange Tip, male, 1988.

D.R. Tye.

Plate 8f: Orange Tip, female, West Hill, 1991.

D.J. Land

Plate 9a: Green Hairstreak, Haldon.

D.R. Tye

Plate 9b: Brown Hairstreak, female, West Hill, 1991.

S.H. Mitchell

Plate 9c: Brown Hairstreak.

D.R. Tye

Plate 9d: Purple Hairstreak, male, Aylesbeare, 1991.

S.H. Mitchell

Plate 9e, Purple Hairstreak.

B.Chatfield

Plate 9f: White-letter Hairstreak, Lynmouth, 1990.

Plate 10a: Small Copper, Haldon, 1983.

Plate 10b: Sooty Copper, male, Ilfracombe, 1887.

Plate 10c: Long-tailed Blue, Kingswear, M.R. Edmonds, 1961.

Plate 10d: Small Blue, Under Hooken, 1973.

Plate 10e: Green-underside Blue, male, Torquay, 1936.

Plate 10f: Brown Argus.

D.J. Land

Plate 11a: Silver-studded Blue, male, East Budleigh Common.

S.H. Mitchell

Plate 11b: Common Blue, female.

RAMM

Plate 11c: Chalk-hill Blue, Zeal Monachorum, 1935.

R. Goodden

Plate 11d: Adonis Blue, 1934 (T. Jenkyn). West of Beer Head, females.

D.J. Land

Plate 11e: Holly Blue, Haldon, 1984.

T. Jenkyn

Plate 11f: Large Blue, female, Hartland, 1971.

H. Land

Plate 12a: White Admiral.

D.E. Bolton

Plate 12b: Red Admiral.

S.H. Mitchell

Plate 12c: Painted Lady.

S.H. Mitchell

Plate 12d: Peacock.

S.H. Mitchell

Plate 12e: Small Tortoiseshell, 1985.

BC (Devon Branch)

Plate 12f: Large Tortoiseshell, Loddiswell, 1942.

S.H. Mitchell

Plate 13a: Pearl-bordered Fritillary.

C.R. Bristow

Plate 13b: Pearl-bordered Fritillary,
Newton Wood, 1987.

S.H. Mitchell

Plate 13c: Small Pearl-bordered Fritillary.

M. Land.

Plate 13d: Small Pearl-bordered Fritillary.

D.E. Bolton

Plate 13e: Marsh Fritillary.

C.R. Bristow

Plate 13f: Marsh Fritillary, Witheridge
Moor, 1988.

D.J. Land

Plate 14a: High Brown Fritillary, Bovey Valley Woods, 1986.

R.A. Tye

Plate 14b: High Brown Fritillary, Dunsford.

D.E. Bolton

Plate 14c: Dark Green Fritillary.

R.A. Tye

Plate 14d: Dark Green Fritillary.

S.H. Mitchell

Plate 14e: Silver-washed Fritillary, male.

D.J. Land

Plate 14f: Silver-washed Fritillary.

BC (Devon Branch)

Plate 15a: Queen of Spain Fritillary, female, 1949, bred from a Stoke Point female.

D.E. Bolton

Plate 15b: Comma.

D.J. Land

Plate 15c: Heath Fritillary, Oakford, 1984.

D.E. Bolton

Plate 15d: Speckled Wood, 1986.

S.H. Mitchell

Plate 15e: Wall.

D.E. Bolton

Plate 15f: Marbled White.

D.J. Land

Plate 16a: Grayling.

S.H. Mitchell

Plate 16b: Gatekeeper, female.

S.H. Mitchell

Plate 16c: Meadow Brown, female.

D.J. Land

Plate 16d: Ringlet.

D.J. Land

Plate 16e: Small Heath.

V.R. Tucker

Plate 16f: Monarch, female, Slapton, 1981.

collection when it was sold in 1939. There were two reasons why Spooner thought that collecting was not a primary cause for the decline; firstly, the species declined in areas where virtually no collecting took place, and secondly, the butterfly persisted in other areas, despite continuous collection. However, although collecting was not the main cause of the decline, it could be the final straw if the population was seriously reduced by other factors.

Climatic effects are more difficult to interpret, because the whole life cycle has to be considered. Conditions favourable for adults are not necessarily those for larvae, nor for the ants on which they depend in their later instars. Clearly, the 1976 and 1977 droughts had a disastrous effect on the last Devon colony, but this was not the primary cause of the extinction, as the population had been severely reduced by other factors.

A third possibility was the loss of the larval foodplant by crowding out, as part of natural ecological succession of heather to scrub, by land improvement through fertilising, excessive burning, too intensive grazing, and by ploughing up. In Devon, crowding out was responsible for the extinction at one of the Dartmoor sites, and was partly responsible for the decline on the south coast. For the period 1865 to 1870, thyme *Thymus praecox* on the south coast was plentiful, interspersed with patches of gorse, but by 1884, there had been such a big change in the vegetation that Bignell (1884a; b) remarked that 'he could have put all he saw [of thyme] into his waistcoat pocket'. The decline was attributed by Bignell and Nicholls (1875) to the intensive burning of gorse and improvement of the rough pasture for grazing (in fact, gorse burning results in an increase in thyme). Ploughing destroyed at least one site in Devon (see above).

The loss of the North Devon colonies was attributed by Thomas (1989) to the direct and indirect effects of myxomatosis. The direct result was the loss of an intensive grazing force, and the consequent invasion of tall grass, scrub etc. The indirect effect was that it became profitable to convert the rough grazing on this marginal farmland to arable. As hillsides became less important for pasture, the old practice of burning the gorse and grass for a better crop was abandoned. The net effect was the cessation of grazing on all the cultivated land along that part of the North Devon coast between the mid-1950s and the late 1970s, and Large Blue numbers plummeted (Thomas, 1989).

A direct corollary of the crowding out, although not realized until recently (see Thomas, 1989), was the early and very important effect on its ant host. Spooner (1963) thought that secondary fluctuations in the *M. arion* populations could be due to the ant hosts. At that time, it was thought that up to four species of the red ant genus *Myrmica*, together with species of other genera, could, with equal success, be host for Large Blue larvae. However, Thomas (1977) showed that although the various species of *Myrmica* accept the caterpillars with equal readiness, they only survive well in the nests of *M. sabuleti*. *M. sabuleti* only dominates the ground in densities needed for the Large Blue on sun-baked, south-facing hillsides where the sward is cropped short and sparse. The ant is quickly shaded out if grazing is abandoned, or even reduced, only to be replaced by another, more tolerant, but usually unsuitable close relative, *M. scabrinodis* (Thomas, 1980). The change from *M. sabuleti* to *M. scabrinodis* occurs quite quickly after grazing is relaxed, whereas thyme persists in a wide range of sward heights, and flourishes under grazing regimes that support either *sabuleti* or *scabrinodis*. After many years, the thyme too declines on ungrazed sites.

### Re-establishment

After several years of management of its old Dartmoor site, a trial began in 1983 to re-establish the Large Blue using Swedish stock (*Maculinea arion arion*) (Thomas, 1989). Ninety eight larvae were released in September 1983. Seven butterflies emerged in 1984; they were 3 to 4 weeks earlier than siblings in Sweden, but this coincided with peak bud production of thyme on the site. At least one female paired and laid eggs, resulting in 2 to 4 adults in 1985; from these, 10 to 12 adults emerged in 1986 (Thomas in Emmet and Heath, 1989). As the experiment appeared to be working, it was decided that a full-scale introduction should be made. Jeremy Thomas and David Simcox went to Sweden and collected several hundred eggs. From these, 200 young caterpillars survived and were scattered over the site to add to the small population from the earlier trial. In 1987, about 75 Large Blues emerged and laid about 2030 eggs. In 1988, adult numbers increased to between 150 and 200. This increase meant that some adults could be removed in an attempt to found a second colony in the West Country. The remaining adults, despite the severe drought, laid 4500 eggs.

It is hoped, that if the experiment is successful, adult numbers will fluctuate between 500 in a poor year and 1000 in a good year. It is also hoped to re-establish the Large Blue at six sites in ten years time, at two of which there will be public access (Thomas, 1989).

## Duke of Burgundy *Hamearis lucina* (Linnaeus)

This species is extinct in Devon, but there is a small colony just over the county boundary in Somerset. Reading (1862) gave two old records: near Dartmouth and Dunsford Wood. Mr G.H. Gush informs us that there used to be a small colony between Paignton and Torquay [very approximately SX8260], but that the site was built over in about 1935. There has been no subsequent confirmed sighting.

# Nymphalidae

## White Admiral *Ladoga camilla* (Linnaeus)        Plate 12a

According to Coxhead (1970), the White Admiral was introduced from Brockenhurst, Hampshire, stock in 1927 into a wood south of Honiton, and that the experiment was a great success as 'it is now firmly established in the area'. Mr G.M. Spooner, however, informs us that this introduction failed.

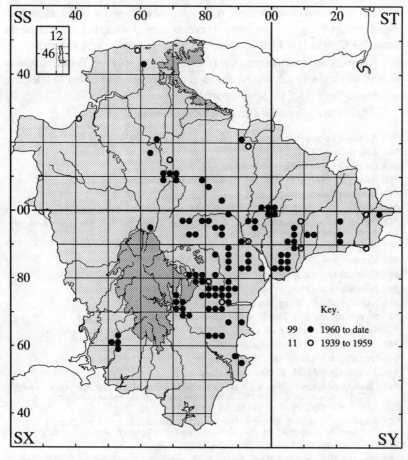

White Admiral (all records)

There is no further record of the White Admiral in Devon until July 22nd 1939 when Woollatt (1943) saw it at a 'well-wooded locality near Exeter' [=Ash-clyst Forest, as confirmed by notes on a 1939 specimen in the Rouden Colln., RAMM], although he was generally disbelieved by the local entomologists of the day. Confirmation of its presence in Ashclyst Forest was by J.R. Parsons on Aug. 16th 1941 (Stidston, 1952), and July 8th 1942 (Woollatt, 1943). However, by then, the second and third Devon White Admirals had been seen at Abbotsham Cliffs [SS4026] in June 1940 by S.M.P. (Dev. Ass.) and Combe Martin [SS5846] (BRC, Monks Wood).

The spread of the White Admiral across Devon was quite rapid, as by the 1950s, it was established in a broad belt through the middle of the county. In the second map, we have plotted the occurrences 1939-1959, by decade, so that its expansion is not masked by its present distribution. The early 1940s sightings in the north-west around Barnstaple did not result in the establishment of colonies, as there has been no subsequent record. Possibly they were just migrating singletons. Similarly, some sightings in recent years, such as the one at Newton House [SX8798] in 1982 by R. Greenway, are strays from nearby colonies.

Expansion of the range of the White Admiral into Plym Forest, first seen in 1970, was a result of human assistance. O.G. Watkins admitted to releasing individuals there (M. Catt, *pers. commn.*).

Below are given all the records for the 1940s and 1950s:

1939, **Ashclyst Forest**, July 22nd, L.H. Woollatt (Woollatt, 1943).

1940, **Abbotsham Cliffs**, June, S.M.P. (Dev. Ass.)

1940, **Combe Martin** (BRC, Monks Wood).

1941, **Ashclyst Forest**, Aug. 6th, J.R. Parsons (Stidston, 1952).

1942, **Ashclyst Forest**, July 8th, L.H. Woollatt (Woollatt, 1943).

1942, **Wonford**, four on July 8th, L.H. Woollatt (Woollatt, 1943; Bracken, 1943).

1942, outskirts of **Newton Abbot** [=Bovey Heath, see Stidston, 1952], mid-July, F.W. Jeffery (Milman, 1943); 1946-48, 1950-51 (Stidston, 1952) and subsequently.

1943, **Shappan Valley, near Barnstaple**, S.M.P. (Dev. Ass.)

1945, **Kenton**, July 13th and 17th, Col. Browse (Anon., 1946).

1945, **Dawlish** (Anon., 1946).

1946, **Fairmile** near Ottery St Mary, Aug. 10th, S.E. Moore.

1946, **Newton Abbot-Bovey Heath** (Stidston, 1952) (see also 1942).

1947, **Nymet Bridge**, July 13th (RAMM) (see also 1955).

1947, **Stover Woods**, 6 - 11 each year up to 1951, A.H. Dobson, and subsequently.

1947, **Drumbridge Bridge**, F.W. Jeffery (Stidston, 1949).

1948, **Drumbridge Bridge**, July 5th, H.G. Hurrell (Stidston, 1949).

1948, **Axminster**, July 7th, K. White (Stidston, 1952).

1948, **Hawkswood**, near Offwell, J.R.W. Coxhead - seen in all subsequent years up to 1972, but not in 1973-75, or 1977. 1965 was described as the best year since 1951; scarce in 1969 (Dev. Ass.; Wallace, 1979).

1949, **Paradise Copse**. The 'Tiverton district' of the Blundell's School Magazine (G.M. Spooner, *pers. commn.*). In 1950, the colony said to be increasing (Stidston, 1952).

1949, **near Cullompton**, July 10th (Stidston, 1950).

1950, **Newte's Hill**, July 24th (Dev. Ass.). This is another of the 'Tiverton district' of Blundells.

1950, **near Chulmleigh**, Aug. 19th, one; Aug. 24th, three, R.D. Turrall (Stidston, 1952).

1950, **Bovey Pottery works**, one, July 29th, S.T. Stidston (Dev. Ass.).

1951, **Drumbridge**, July 17th, H.G. Hurrell (P. Jeffery, *pers. commn.*).

1952, **Teigngrace**, July 22nd, F.C. Fenton (Stidston, 1953).

1952, **Bovey Tracey**, July 25th (also July 30th 1955), F.C. Fenton (Stidston, 1953).

1953, **Kingsteignton clay pits**, July 27th, 'took my first Devonshire specimens' S.T. Stidston (Dev. Ass.).

1954, **Stover Lake**, July 11th, G.M. Spooner; June 30th 1959, A.H. Dobson (Dev. Ass.).

1954-55, **Newton Poppleford**, R.C.J. (Dev. Ass.).

1955, **near Bickleigh**, three, July 25th, G.R.M. (Dev. Ass.).

1955, **Stover Woods**, July 20th, C.W. Holcroft (RAMM).

1955, **Nymet Wood**, July 15th and 17th, C.W. Holcroft (RAMM); see also 1947.

1956, **Haldon**, one on July 22nd, A.S.W. (Dev. Ass.).

1956, **Rousdon**, two, A.S.B. (Dev. Ass.).

1957, **Lustleigh Cleave**, June 27th, D.N. Woodland.

1959, **Rousdon Landslip**, July, A.G. Tomlinson (Wallace, 1967).

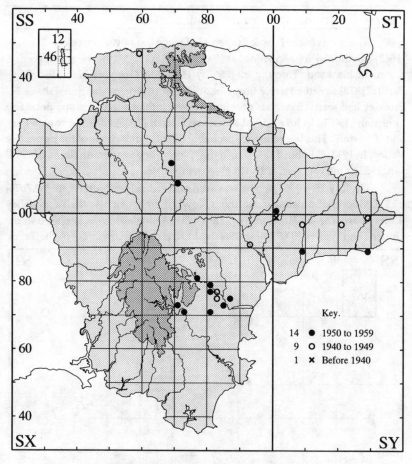

White Admiral (first records, by decade)

It is generally thought that the successful expansion of the White Admiral was in part related to the cessation of woodland management during the 1930s and later years, especially during the Second World War. The decline in management, which is detrimental to many woodland species, benefitted the White Admiral by allowing good growths of the larval foodplant, honeysuckle *Lonicera periclymenum*, to develop. However, it appears that climate was also a major factor during that time. A succession of warm Junes throughout the 1930s was beneficial to *camilla*, as this meant that the duration of the larval and pupal stages were reduced, with a consequent reduction in predation, and an increase in adult numbers (Emmet and Heath, 1989).

The White Admiral flies generally from the second week of July to the third week of August. The earliest adult seen is May 27th 1990 (R. Khan) and latest, Aug. 27th.

## Purple Emperor *Apatura iris* (Linnaeus)

The status of the Purple Emperor in Devon has never been clear. Reading (1862) mentioned its occurrence at 'Barnstaple' (G.F. Mathew), and there is a record in Bigwood, Torquay in 1866 by Horndon (Torquay Nat. Hist. Soc.). Parfitt (1878) saw the Purple Emperor at Dunsford Bridge and noted that a Mr Prowley had seen it in woods near Starcross. A dubious record is mentioned by Longstaff (1907b) in July 1903 at Mortehoe. Barrett (1906) adds Newnham Park and 'Tiverton'. This last reference probably refers to the woods of the upper Exe Valley. In 1911, C.E. Burd saw one in the Avon valley near South Brent (Nicholson, 1933). One was seen at Dartington in July 1945.

On July 25th 1951, a pair was seen at Newbridge, Poundsgate [SX7070] by S.E. Moore, who also saw one 'flying slowly in front of me' in the Teign Valley under Sharp Tor [SX7189] on Aug. 12th 1951. A singleton was also seen in the Upper Teign Valley [SX8088] in 1986 by M.R. Hughes. Lower down the Teign,

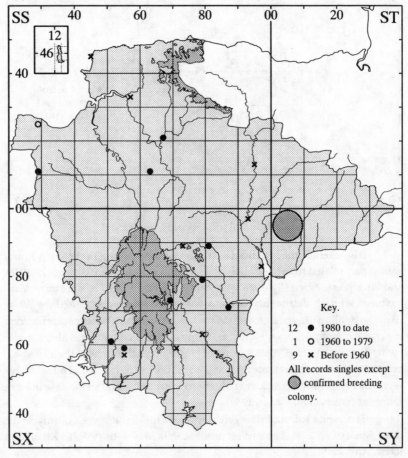

Purple Emperor

the Purple Emperor is stated to have been seen in Hisley Wood [SX7780] (Anon., 1988), but P. Page informs us that this statement is probably based on sightings in 1979 and 1980 by R. Khan in Pullabrook Wood; none has been seen since. These last three records, coupled with Parfitt's earlier sighting, suggest that there is a small colony in the upper part of the Teign Valley. Should a colony exist there, then the prospects for its continued existence are high, since many of the woods bordering the valley are natural broad-leafed deciduous ones in the hands of various conservation bodies (Woodland Trust, English Nature, Devon Wildlife Trust, and National Trust).

A colony, known to have existed in the Hartland area [SS2824] in the 1940s and 50s (G.H. Gush), persisted until at least 1973, when a singleton was observed by A. Archer-Lock.

Another colony survived in Stoke Woods, Exeter, until about 1950 (R. Khan).

There is possibly a colony at Higher Hollocombe [SS6210] where males were seen by R. Bulcraig in August 1985.

One was seen at Padeley, Kings Nympton [SS6721] by S. Young in 1988.

Possible sightings in 1987 included Great Shaugh Wood [SX5160] (T.D. Sleep) and Newnham Valley [SX5559] (M. Olver), at Tamar Lake [SS2911] by F. Bridle ('dark-winged butterfly with a lovely violet blue colour') and Decoy, Newton Abbot [SX8670] (two doubtful sightings) (information from K. Bastow). The Newnham Valley occurrence is interesting as this is a locality referred to by Barrett (1906) for the Purple Emperor. M. Olver informs us that 5 larvae were found in 1987, but these are thought to have been introduced by a dealer from Cornwall.

Devon's best-known Purple Emperor colony is in a wood in which specific management for it, by planting sallows *Salix* spp., is carried out by the Forestry Commission. The size of the colony is uncertain, but it is not large.

The status of another colony is uncertain. In 1985, G.H. Gush saw four males on July 4th, at least twelve males on July 17th, three females egg laying on Broad-leafed Sallow *S. caprea* on July 20th and one battered male on Buddleia on Aug. 5th. There was no further sighting until 1990, when one male and five females were seen; one female seen in 1991.

Following Burd's sighting in 1911, adults were again seen in the Avon Valley [SX5070] in 1992 (M. Catt, *pers. commn.*).

---

# Red Admiral *Vanessa atalanta* (Linnaeus)                    Plate 12b

The Red Admiral is an annual migrant that occasionally overwinters as an adult, and has even been known to breed throughout the winter. This occurred at Beesands and Lannacombe in 1989/90 (M. Catt, *pers. commn.*). Those individuals that do survive the winter, emerge in early spring, but the migrants do not generally arrive until late May. The species breeds readily in this country. The larvae feed on Stinging Nettle *Urtica dioica*, Small Nettle *U. urens*, Hop

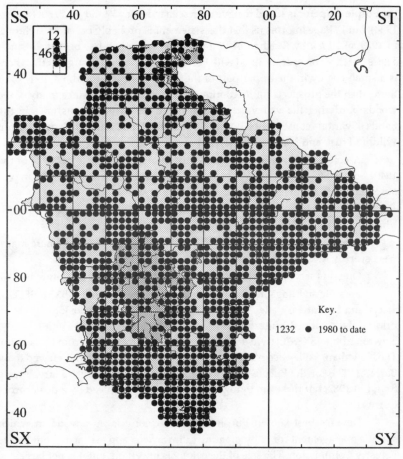

Red Admiral

*Humulus lupulus* and Pellitory-of-the Wall *Parietaria judaica*. Adults fly throughout autumn, and into December if the weather is fine. They are generally the last butterflies to be seen during the year. Adults are a common sight on Buddleia, and later in the year, on Ivy *Hedera helix* flowers.

## Painted Lady *Cynthia cardui* (Linnaeus)                    Plate 12c

This species is an irregular immigrant that sometimes has years of abundance - 1985 and 1988 were two of the last such years. Following a year with only three sightings, 1985 started with a remarkably early immigration in March (3rd and 4th) and April. 1987 ended (or 1988 began) with an immigration of Painted Ladies along the south coast of Devon and Dorset. It was first recorded in Devon on Dec. 22nd, with subsequent sightings in January and February.

Immigrants readily breed in Britain, with the larval foodplants being thistles, especially Spear Thistle *Cirsium vulgare*, Creeping Thistle *C. arvense*,

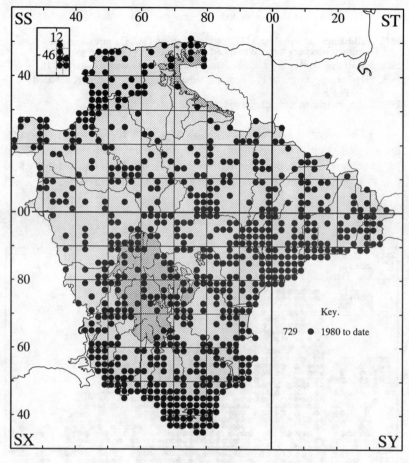

Key.

729 ● 1980 to date

Painted Lady

Marsh Thistle *C. palustre* and Slender Thistle *Carduus tenuiflorus*. The Stinging Nettle *Urtica dioica*, Viper's Bugloss *Echium vulgare*, Lesser Burdock *Arctium minus* and Pellitory-of-the-Wall *Parietaria judaica* are sometimes used.

## Scarce Painted Lady *Cynthia virginiensis* (Drury)

Only four specimens of this North American species have been recorded in Devon, with a fifth being taken just over the border at Torpoint in 1876. All were seen between August and October. It was originally thought that British examples were imports of adults or immature stages. It is now thought that the Scarce Painted Lady is a genuine immigrant. North America is the most likely source, but some may have originated from the Canary Islands which were colonised by *virginiensis* in 1805, from where it has recently spread to Spain and Portugal (Bretherton in Emmet and Heath, 1989).

The following Devon records are known:

1942, **Walkhampton**, Sept. 24th, O.G. Watkins (Jeffery, 1942; Dannreuther, 1943). This specimen was very tattered as it had passed though a threshing machine.

1970, **Braunton Burrows**, Aug. 26th, B. Goater and D.J.L. Agassiz (Goater, 1971).

1970, **Yelverton**, Sept. 18th, A.P. Gainsford, female caught on Buddleia (Gainsford, 1971, pl. ii).

1972, **Bishopsteignton**, Oct. 4th, caught on Buddleia (Coleridge, 1973).

The Torpoint specimen, caught on Sept. 20th 1876, is said to be in the Bignell Collection in the Plymouth City Museum (Emmet and Heath, 1989, p. 197), but there is also a specimen from Anthony House, Torpoint, caught by Miss C.L. Pole on Sept. 20th 1876 in the Hope Entomological Collections.

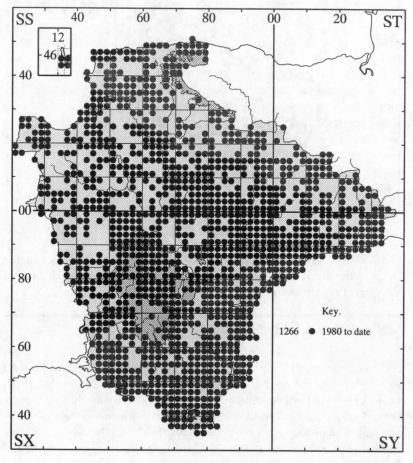

Small Tortoiseshell

## Small Tortoiseshell *Aglais urticae* (Linnaeus)　　　Plate 12e

The Small Tortoiseshell is common and widely distributed; adults range extensively. It probably occurs in every tetrad, with the possible exception of some of the higher ground of Dartmoor. It is one of the first butterflies to be seen in the spring, although as they overwinter as adults, they may be seen on warm days during winter. The new brood emerges in about mid-June, and a second brood (the one that will overwinter) in September. The latter brood remains infertile until the spring.

The foodplant is the Stinging Nettle *Urtica dioica*, on which the webs of the caterpillars can be easily spotted.

## Large Tortoiseshell *Nymphalis polychloros* (Linnaeus) Plate 12f

The Large Tortoiseshell is probably extinct as a breeding species. Recent scattered sightings (if authentic) are presumably migrants or releases. The Large Tortoiseshell was fairly common in the middle of the nineteenth century, with its capture receiving little comment (Mathew, 1858a; Dell, 1858; Rawlinson 1858). Yet Reading (1862) and Bignell (in Newman, 1869) referred only to singletons at the following localities: Sidmouth, Totnes, Wembury, Bickleigh Vale, Milehouse and Stoke, Buckfastleigh, Axminster, and between Plymouth Station and Plymbridge. Morris (1876) mentioned the occurrence of *polychloros* in woods on the banks of the River Dart. Parfitt (1878) remarked that the Large Tortoiseshell was very generally distributed, but not at all common. Some time after 1878, it appears to have become scarcer in Devon, with only widely distributed observations, mostly singletons, during the next 70-80 years. Barrett (1893) stated that it was 'very scarce in Devon', and then later (1906) listed Exeter, Dawlish (probably based on Rawlinson, 1858), Seaton, Topsham, Barnstaple (probably Mathew, 1858a), Ilfracombe, Ivybridge and Bickleigh Vale as localities for the Large Tortoiseshell, but made no comment about its status.

There are confirmed records of breeding in the county at the beginning of the century (Seaton in 1902; ?Teignmouth in 1902; Torquay in 1908). Rogers (1903) stated that the Large Tortoiseshell 'appeared to be on the increase during the last few years'. Specimens caught by Milman in 1918 (Lees Colln., Dev. Ass.) and from the observations of Mayor (1919b) and Whitley (1919), suggest a small colony near Paignton in the early part of the twentieth century, although it was described as 'decidedly scarce in those parts'. The cluster of records in the Plym valley during 1945 to 1949 suggests a small colony; this may have survived until 1954, and would have been the last breeding colony in the county.

Care has to be taken to distinguish the Large and Small tortoiseshells; some Small Tortoiseshells can appear 'large'. On the hind part of the Large Tortoiseshell forewing, there are four (not three) black spots, two of which are much larger than those on the Small Tortoiseshell. Because of the possibility of confusion of the two species, sightings cannot be accepted uncritically. All unsubstantiated records have been rejected; others, which on questioning the recorders, appear to be Large Tortoiseshells, nevertheless lack the proof of a photograph. For this reason, it is difficult to ascertain the current status of the species.

The following records are additional to those mentioned above:

1858, **Pilton**, March (Mathew, 1858a).

1858, **Bickleigh Vale** (Dell, 1858).

1858, **Dawlish** (Rawlinson, 1858).

1866, **Newton Abbot (Milber Down)**, August (Dev. Ass.).

1871, **Plympton**, Oct. 6th (HEC, ex-colln. Meldola).

pre-1874, **Kingsbridge**, Nicholls, (Fox, 1874).

1889, **Sidmouth** - 'one or two specimens, but by no means common' (Majendie, 1891).

1893, **Westward Ho!**, July, E.M. Eustace (Dev. Ass.).

1895, between **Sidmouth and Honiton**, July 17th (Prideaux, 1896).

1896, **Dartmouth**, July 11th (HEC, ex-colln. Hamm).

1899, **Bovey Tracey**, July 19th (HEC, ex-colln. Hamm).

?1900, **Dawlish** - one adult only seen, ?August (Turner, 1901) - same specimen as that below?

1900, **Dawlish**, Aug. 12th (HEC, ex-colln. Hamm).

1900, **The Decoy**, Aug. 12th (HEC, ex-colln. Hamm).

1900, **Lee**, Ilfracombe (Longstaff, 1907b).

1901, **Lifton** (Bracken, 1946).

1901, **Exeter**, Kenbury Lane, July (Solly, 1932).

1902, **Exeter**, Kenbury Lane, August (Solly, 1932).

1902, **Seaton**, P.P. Milman - 'larvae bred'. Two specimens in the Lees Collection from Seaton, dated July 24th and 26th 1902, collected by (or from the collection of) R. South, may be these specimens.

1902, ?**Teignmouth** - 3 larval nests, two on elm and one on Sallow (Rogers, 1903).

1903, **Dawlish**, late July/early August, 1 specimen (Brown, 1904).

1904, **Twitchen, Mortehoe**, Oct. 2nd (Longstaff, 1907b).

c.1908, **Torquay**, 'Imagines frequent, larvae more common' (Dev. Ass.).

1911, **Bickleigh Vale**, S.T. Stidston.

1918, **Paignton**, July 28th, P.P. Milman (Lees Colln.).

1919, **Bovey Tracey**, July (BRC, Monks Wood).

1919, **Paignton**, Aug. 10th (Whitley, 1919).

1921, **Yealm district**, S.T. Stidston.

1921, **Erme district**, S.T. Stidston.

c.1924, **Kenn and Dawlish**, E.D. Morgan.

1926, **Exeter** (Bracken, 1940).

1926, **Bideford** (Bracken, 1940).

1926, **Torquay** (Bracken, 1940).

1927, **Chudleigh**, Aug. 17th, S.T. Stidston (Stidston, 1952).

1928, **Erme district**, S.T. Stidston.

1935, **Chudleigh**, May 5th, F.W. Jeffery (Stidston, 1952).

1936, **Bideford**, September (Bracken, 1940).

1936, **Dawlish** (BRC, Monks Wood).

1938, **Chudleigh Bridge**, May 21st, F.W. Jeffery (Bracken, 1940).

1942, **Loddiswell**, Aug. 6th and Sept. 13th, F.W. Jeffery (Doe, 1942) (BC, Devon Branch).

1942, **'Tiverton'** [=Oakford Rectory], May 2nd, E.M. Kelly (Doe, 1942; Bracken, 1943).

1944, **Maidencombe, Torquay**, July 31st, F.H. Lees (Lees Colln).

1945, **Dewerstone, Shaugh**, April 9th, O.G. Watkins (Bracken, 1945).

1945, **Bickleigh Vale**, April 21st, O.G. Watkins (Bracken, 1945).

1945, **Exeter**, September, R.M. Prideaux (Stidston, 1952).

1945, **Dawlish** (BRC, Monks Wood).

1945, **Woolacombe - Mortehoe** (BRC, Monks Wood).

1945, **Plympton St Maurice**, April 2nd, W. Harcourt Bath (Bracken, 1946).

1946, **Newton Ferrers**, April 2nd, D. Hunt (Stidston, 1952).

1946, **Plym Bridge**, April 30th, G.M. Spooner (Stidston, 1952).

1946, **Sidmouth**, July 8th (Aldridge, 1946).

1946, **Bere Alston**, July 14th (F.W. Jeffery manuscript).

1946, **Staverton**, two on July 27th-29th, E.T. Hamlyn (Stidston, 1952).

c.1946, **Dartington**, Mr Martin (Bracken, 1947).

1947, **Plym Bridge**, June 12th, G.M. Spooner (Imms in Bracken, 1948).

1947, **Bovey Tracey**, August, W.H. Scott (Bracken, 1943).

1948, **Lydford**, R.C.L. Perkins (Stidston, 1949).

1948, **Plym Bridge**, March 27th, R. Haynes (P. Jeffery, *pers. commn.*).

1949, **Plym Bridge**, March 26th, G.M. Spooner (Stidston, 1950).

1954, **Plym Bridge**, March 26th, R. Haynes (Western Morning News).

1954, **Newton Poppleford**, February, 'one seen, not taken', R.C.J. (Dev. Ass.).

1957, **Torbryan**, June 30th, V.C. Almy (Dev. Ass.).

1964, **Yelverton**, Aug. 20th, E.D. Leech (*Field*, Aug. 20th 1964, p. 392; Turner, 1966).

1966, **Raleigh Estate**, September, (BRC, Plymouth).

1968, **Westhill**, two seen Sept. 10th, E.D. Tallant (Turner, 1969).

1968, **Mortehoe**, Aug. 23rd (BRC, Monks Wood).

1972, **Galmpton**, September, C.P. Davey (Turner, 1973).

1973, **Woolacombe** (BRC, Monks Wood).

1984, **Woolston Green, Staverton**, K.A. Westcott.

1985, **Appledore**, Aug. 8th, B. Price.

1985, **Higher Hollocombe**, June 16th, July 27th and August, R. Bulcraig.

1985, **Coombe Farm, Beaworthy**, G.J. Barnes 'worn specimen, caught, examined and released'.

1985, **Exeter**, April 9th, P. Tapp.

1988, **Bovey Tracey**, Sept. 15th, M. Wright 'on buddleia with three Small Tortoiseshells; had 4 spots on forewing, lacked the blue of the latter'.

The larval foodplants are chiefly Elm *Ulmus* spp., Sallow *Salix cinerea*, and Willow *Salix* spp. The butterfly hibernates as an adult. Offspring of the hibernating generation usually emerge at the beginning of July, and it is these adults which will overwinter.

## Camberwell Beauty *Nymphalis antiopa* (Linnaeus)

This is a distinctive, irregular, scarce immigrant from Europe. The great invasions of 1872 and 1976 were clearly the results of immigration from northwest Europe, since most records were from eastern Britain (Emmet and Heath, 1989, fig. 51b). There is no record of a Camberwell Beauty for either of these years in Devon. Bretherton (in Emmet and Heath, 1989; *pers. commn.*) suggests that the scatter of records over the years along the south coast suggests that most of those specimens originated in southern Europe. Beware, however, breeders of the species have been known to release stock!

The earliest record for the county is at East Ogwell sometime before 1830 (Turton and Kingston, 1830).

The complete record for the county follows:

pre-1830, **East Ogwell** (Turton and Kingston, 1830).

1858, **Devonport**, August 15th (Dele, 1858).

1858, **Torquay**, Sept. and Dec. 12th (Battersby, 1859).

pre-1862, **Barnstaple**, G.F. Mathew (Reading, 1862).

1865, **Ilfracombe**, Oct. 9th, Mrs F. Smith (Smith, 1865).

1867, **Hele, Ilfracombe**, Aug. 31st (Longstaff, 1867; 1907b).

*c.*1868, **Plympton**, Dr Gildard (Parfitt, 1878).

pre-1878, **Plymouth** (Parfitt, 1878).

1873, **Brixham**, G.C. Bignell (Parfitt, 1878).

1880, **Plymouth**, G.C. Bignell (Heath, 1946).

1889, **Sidmouth**, Aug. 17th, (Majendie, 1891).

1892, **Torquay** (Lupton, 1911).

1900, **Rock Walk, Torquay**, May (Walker, 1930).

*c.*1900, **Chittlehampton**, T.M. Cardus (Longstaff, 1907b).

pre-1906, **Bideford** (Barrett, 1906).

pre-1906, **Honiton** (Barrett, 1906).

1901, **Dartmoor**, August, (Phillips, 1901).

1901, **Tavistock**, Sept. 20th, H. Kerslake (Phillips, 1901).

1902, **Grimspound**, August 15th (W.D. Kirby, 1903).

1929/30. **Blackdown Camp**, W. Chaplin-Bennett (Anon. 1931).

1938, **Exmouth**, Aug. 9th, H. Henstock (Stidston, 1952).

1944, **Tavistock**, several August, M. Allport (Wallis, 1944); October (Bracken, 1945).

1949, **Devon**, Sept. 4th (Dannreuther, 1950).

1952, **Northam,** July 15th, M.F. Pollock (Western Morning News, July 17th 1952; French, 1953).

1952, **Tamerton Foliot**, Aug. 18th, P. Goodfellow (Western Morning News, Oct. 6th 1952; French, 1953).

1956, **Combe Martin**, Sept. 23rd (French, 1957).

1957, **Exeter**, September (Dev. Ass.; French, 1958).

1959, **Exeter**, Aug. 30th (French, 1960).

1967, **Cullompton**, July 28th, M. Winterflood (Turner, 1968).

1976, **Lynmouth**, Aug. 22nd, L.R. Denman (Chalmers-Hunt, 1977).

1980, **Start Point**, Sept. 21st, J. Huggins (Huggins, 1983).

1985, **Exeter**, Aug. 7th, M.E. Simmonds.

1985, **Northam**, Aug. 17th, C. Webb.

1991, **Bystock Reserve**, March 6th, J. Turner - one of several specimens released about two weeks earlier.

1992, **Combe Martin**, July, M. Hart.

# Peacock *Inachis io* (Linnaeus)       Plate 12d

The same remarks apply to the Peacock as to the Small Tortoiseshell, although the Peacock has been recorded on fewer tetrads, possibly because the adult flight period is shorter. The Peacock is single-brooded, with the overwintering females egg laying from March through to June. The Peacock, in our experience, tends to hibernate on average a month earlier than the Small Tortoiseshell, but emerges from hibernation at about the same time.

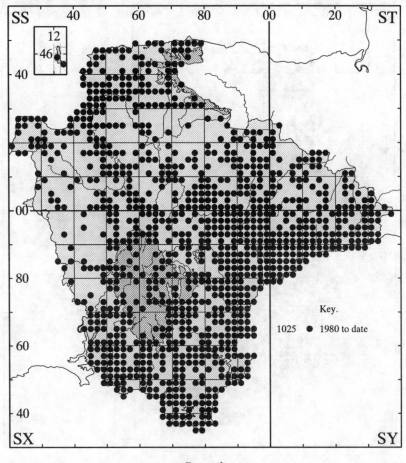

SS  40    60    80    00    20  ST

12
-46

40

-00

80

Key.

1025  ● 1980 to date

60

40

SX                                    SY

Peacock

---

**Comma** *Polygonia c-album* (Linnaeus)                    Plate 15b

The Comma was exceedingly scarce in Devon throughout the nineteenth century. The supposed first record of the Comma in Devon was, according to Bracken (1934; 1936), seen by J. Reading in 1855 at Wembury, with additional records at Plymouth in 1861 and 1862, but this was an error, as Bracken had in fact mis-read Reading (1862), and erroneously quoted the section on the Silver-spotted Skipper. Two specimens seen at Dartmouth on Oct. 5th 1868 (Mathew, 1868) are the earliest Devon record. Parfitt (1878) knew only of the Dartmouth record, although there was a pre-1877 record for Lundy Isle (Heaven, in Chanter, 1877). F.D. Welch took two in 1893-1894 at Devonport (Bracken, 1936).

In the early part of the twentieth century, the Comma began to expand from its stronghold in the Welsh Borders, and by 1916 it was widely distributed in Somerset (Pratt, 1986). By the 1920s, the Comma began to appear sparingly in east and south-east Devon. The first twentieth century record that we have for

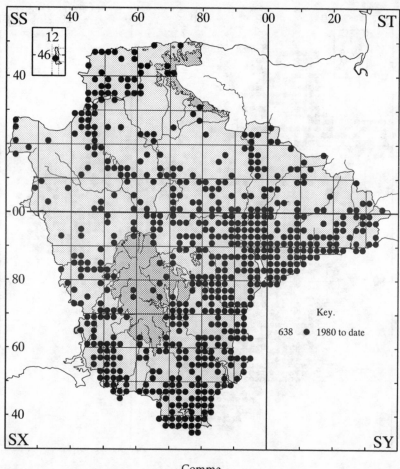

Comma

Devon is July 12th 1920 near Cockington (S.E. Moore), a year earlier than the previously published date (Pratt, 1986, p. 244). Harris (in Doe, 1930) mentioned an unlocated Devon specimen in 1922. Stidston (1952) observed that the Comma was recorded very sparingly up to 1925, when the species began to spread westwards. In 1926, there were sightings at Offwell (and up to 1930) (Tuke, 1932) and Shiphay near Torquay (S.E. Moore). Mr Moore saw another singleton in 1928 at Edginswell near Torquay. Also in 1928, one was seen at South Brent by a Mr Pritchard, who also saw it there 'years ago' (Bracken, 1936), and at Buckerell near Honiton (Harris, in Doe, 1930). Harris also mentioned an unlocated sighting in 1929. It was also seen near Sidmouth on July 19th 1929 (Croft, 1929).

By 1930, the Comma had become more widespread, and it was remarked that for the season 1929-30, the Comma 'seems now well established in South Devon' (Anon., 1931). In that year, specimens were seen at Fordlands near Exeter (Solly, 1932), at Torquay (presumably the one reported in Anon., 1931), between

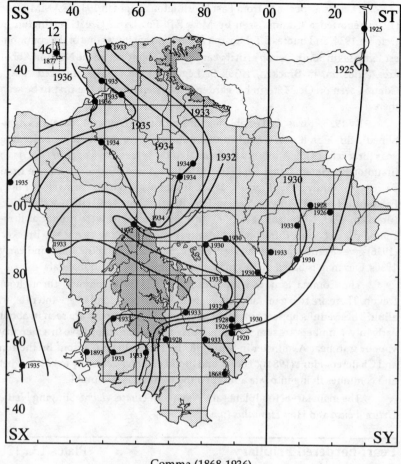

Comma (1868-1936)

Ladram Bay and Budleigh Salterton (S.E. Moore), and at Starcross (also one caught in 1931) (Studd Colln.). A Comma seen at Steps Bridge on March 21st 1931 is presumed to have hibernated and arrived there in 1930.

According to Bracken (1936), the Comma had reached Okehampton, and just crossed into North Devon, by 1932, but it was unknown in the Braunton area (Wright, 1932).

In 1933, in addition to its 1932 localities, the Comma was recorded at Ashburton, Bovey, Chudleigh, Ilfracombe, Ivybridge woods, Newton Abbot, Ottery St Mary, Plympton, Topsham, Totnes, Torquay, Woodbury and Yelverton (Doe, 1934). At Ivybridge, over 30 were seen on Sept. 11th (Bracken, 1936); over two dozen were seen at Woodbury where it was 'becoming more common than formerly' (Henstock, 1934). There was also the first Cornish records in 1933, at Launceston (Nicholson, 1935a) and Polyphant (Frost and Madge, 1991).

There is a specimen from East Worlington caught in 1934 (RAMM). Doe (1935) reported a Comma seen by Miss E.P. Fowler at Great Torrington in October 1934, and quotes S.T. Stidston as saying 'that it was one of the commonest *Vanessas* in South Devon in that year' - it was 'abundant' in the Newton Abbot area (Stidston, in Bracken, 1936). St Leger-Gordon (1934) remarked that a Comma seen on Oct. 16th in his garden at Sticklepath, was the first to be seen there.

By 1935, it was well established in south-west Devon (12 localities mentioned), although it was remarked that numbers were down on the preceding year (Bracken, 1935). A locality additional to those listed by Bracken (1935) is a Braunton specimen, dated Sept. 1st 1935 (Ilfracombe Museum) and one from Barnstaple in July 1935 (Bracken, 1936). It was also seen in Cornwall at Bude, Falmouth, Looe, Luxulyan Valley, Par, Redruth, St Kew Highway in 1935 (Bracken, 1935; Nicholson, 1935b; c). In 1936, specimens were caught at Ilfracombe on Oct. 10th (Ilfracombe Museum) and at Instow (RAMM). Bracken (1936) gives a crude map of the westward expansion during the 1920s and early 1930s. Our map is based on this map, but incorporates additional data.

The Comma is now widespread and relatively common throughout Devon. There are two generations a year, of which the second overwinters as an adult. These adults appear sparingly in spring; their progeny are seen in about early July. Numbers are sometimes reinforced by immigration (two in a mercury vapour trap near Axminster in Sept. 1983 by E.C. Pelham-Clinton (Bretherton and Chalmers-Hunt (1984)). The second brood emerges generally in late August and continues flying into late autumn if the weather is favourable.

The main larval foodplants are Wych Elm *Ulmus glabra*, Stinging Nettle *Urtica dioica*, and Hop *Humulus lupulus*.

## Pearl-bordered Fritillary
*Boloria euphrosyne* (Linnaeus)

Plates 13a,13b

This is one of the commoner of the 'small' fritillaries, and the earliest to appear. It occurs on rough common land with woods nearby, and in woods with open rides and glades. It is well worth searching likely areas for it during the spring.

Its early appearance is one way of distinguishing it from the Small Pearl-bordered Fritillary. Adults in April and May are likely to be the former, as are worn specimens from mid-June onwards. Fresh specimens from mid-June and July are probably the Small Pearl-bordered Fritillary. On the underside, the Pearl-bordered Fritillary has only one silvery spot in the centre of the wing, whereas the Small Pearl-bordered Fritillary has several, and each spot is edged with a heavier black border - see plates.

The foodplants are various species of Violet *Viola* spp.; larvae have also been recorded on Primrose *Primula vulgaris*.

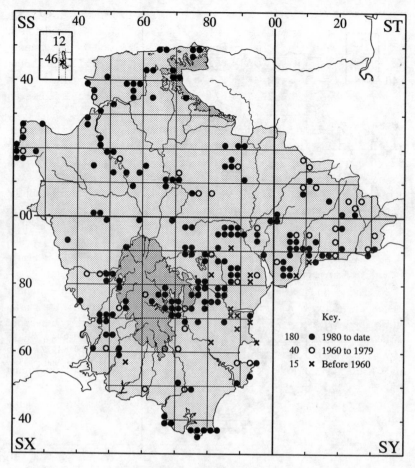

Pearl-bordered Fritillary

The Pearl-bordered Fritillary usually flies from the second week in May (occasionally at the end of April - April 15th 1945 at Torquay (Ford, 1945b)), until early July. Some adults emerge on the South Devon coast in Sept/Oct (M. Catt, *pers. commn.*), but it is not known whether these result in successful broods.

## Small Pearl-bordered Fritillary
*Boloria selene* ([Denis & Schiffermüller])

Plates 13c, 13d

This species appears to be slightly more common than the Pearl-bordered Fritillary. The distinguishing features between the two have already been discussed - see Pearl-bordered Fritillary. The larvae also feed on *Viola* species.

The adults fly from early June (April 29th in 1957, F.W. Jeffery) to mid-July. Occasionally (1911, 1933, 1934, 1949, 1957, 1961, 1964, 1967, 1969, 1973, 1980, 1984 and 1986-1990, 1992) a partial second brood emerges, usually in late August and early September (Sept. 17th 1961, E.J. Hare), although in 1987, fresh,

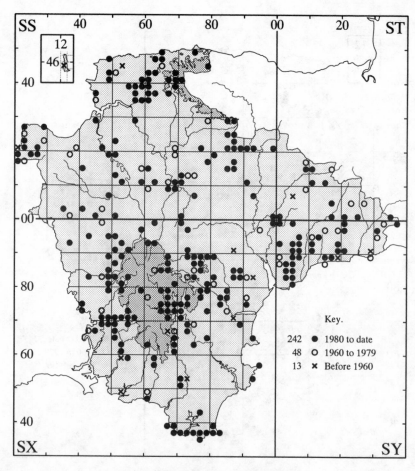

Small Pearl-bordered Fritillary

Key.

242 ● 1980 to date
48 ○ 1960 to 1979
13 ✕ Before 1960

presumed second brood, specimens were flying in early August at several localities.

## Queen of Spain Fritillary *Argynnis lathonia* (L.)    Plate 15a

This is a very rare migrant that occasionally turns up in late August and early September (cf. Scarce Painted Lady, Monarch, Long-tailed Blue).

The complete Devon record is as follows:

**'Devonshire'**, August 1823 (HEC, ex-colln. Sequeira).

**Rosebery Wood**, 1836, Exeter, R. Dawson (Lighton, 1843; Newman, 1869).

**Bystock**, c1853, (several), W. Buller (D'Urban, 1865).

**Braunton Burrows**, 1856 (Mathew, 1857).

**Musbury**, 1866, (3 specimens), J.N. Still (Barrett, 1893).

**Kenton (Oxton)**, Sept. 11th 1871, Studd Collection (RAMM) - possibly the 'Exton' locality of Barrett (1906).

**Barnstaple,** pre-1878 (Parfitt, 1878) - probably the Braunton Burrows record of Mathew (1857).

**Bovey Tracey,** pre-1878, Z.J. Edwards (Parfitt, 1878).

**Braunton Burrows near** *Barnstaple* [our italics], pre-1906 (Barrett, 1906) - probably the Braunton Burrows locality of G.F. Mathew.

**North Devon,** July 7th 1931, N.H. Joy (Joy, 1931).

**Alphington,** Aug. 8th 1935, J.R. Parsons (Stidston, 1952).

**Buckland Monachorum,** Sept. 1st 1947, J.G.M. Scott (Scott, 1947; Bracken, 1948).

**South Devon,** variously given as 'mouth of River Yealm', Sept. 4th 1949 (Stidston, 1950); 'Stoke Point, River Yealm' (Stidston, 1952) and 'Hilsea Point' (O.G. Watkins, *pers. commn.*). Fertile ova were obtained from this female and imagines bred (emerged Nov. 23rd) (O.G. Watkins, *pers. commn.*; Chalmers-Hunt (1983); Hyde (1983)). Some specimens in F.W. Jeffery Collection (BC, Devon Branch) (Plate 15a).

**Higher Metcombe,** Sept. 3rd 1950, E. Thomas (Holroyd, 1952).

**Exeter,** Barrack Road, June 1954, R.E. Melton.

**Bideford,** July 8th 1967 (French, 1971).

**Wembury,** Aug. 27th 1976 (Bretherton, 1983).

**The Warren, Bolt Head,** female, Sept. 21st 1991 (Catt, 1992).

---

# Aphrodite Fritillary *Argynnis aphrodite* (Fabricius)

This North American species is included in Parfitt's (1878) list based on a specimen reputedly caught by Dr Jordan in Bradley Wood near Newton Abbot, details of which were given to Parfitt by J.C. Dale. However, Dale added a question mark after the name.

One other British specimen is known - one taken near Leamington, Warwickshire in 1833 (Emmet and Heath, 1989).

---

# High Brown Fritillary                    Plates 14a, 14b
## *Argynnis adippe* ([Denis & Schiffermüller])

The High Brown Fritillary is similar to the Dark Green Fritillary on the upper surface, but has a slightly concave forewing margin (c.f. slightly convex in the Dark Green Fritillary). The underside is not so deep a green as the latter and, diagnostically, there is a chain of silver-centered red spots towards the outer margin. Nevertheless, confusion of the two species occurs, and submitted records are subject to scrutiny.

Reading (1862) listed Bickleigh Vale, Roborough Down, Shaugh, Morwell Rocks, Exeter, Torquay and Bovey Tracey as localities for this species. Newman (1869) added 'near Newton Abbot' on the evidence of J. Hellins. Parfitt (1878) noted that 'it is by no means a common insect', and that it frequented the borders of woods in similar localities to the Silver-washed Fritillary. Barrett (1906) recorded that it was far less common than the Silver-washed Fritillary, and listed it from Exeter, Stoke, Bickleigh Vale, Honiton, Barnstaple, Instow and the Dartmoor woodlands. Stidston (1952) stated that it was 'Not common. Frequents wooded areas, especially around Dartmoor' and then gave 17 sites where it had occurred between 1930 and 1950. According to Dobson (1969), the High Brown Fritillary was confined to Dartmoor.

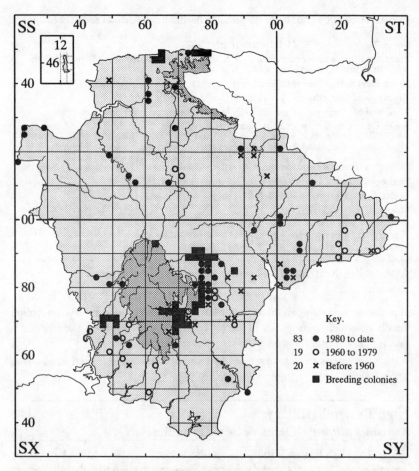

**High Brown Fritillary**

Nationally, *adippe* has declined more rapidly in the last twenty years than any other British butterfly. Over most of its former range, it frequented recently cleared woodland (e.g. coppice), much like the Pearl-bordered Fritillary. Nearly all the woodland colonies, however, have been lost as management has changed or ceased, leaving most of the few remaining colonies, including those in Devon, breeding on violets *Viola* spp. below bracken on south-facing slopes or in valley bottoms. In such situations, usually below the 250m contour, where violets grow at high density among bracken litter, larvae can find their exacting climatic requirements. These include being able to sunbathe in early spring and find shade in early summer. In unmanaged or poorly grazed sites, the build up of bracken litter leads to inadequate violet densities, whereas trampling, especially by cattle and ponies, helps to break it down, to the benefit of violets and High Brown Fritillaries.

The south Dartmoor 'population', based on four river valleys, is now recognised as the second most important in Britain. However, even there, it is highly vulnerable and apparently declining; conservation measures are urgently required. Bracken cutting or rotational small-scale burning may help in some situations, but the most important requirement is the reinstatement of appropriate grazing regimes on neglected and poorly grazed sites.

While Dartmoor is still its principal haunt, it does occur elsewhere. During the 1980s, the High Brown Fritillary was recorded on 62 tetrads. From the distribution map, it can be seen that there are eight areas where the High Brown Fritillary breeds at the present day. Although breeding undoubtedly occurs outside these areas, the presence of a 'spot' on the map does not necessarily indicate a breeding colony.

Below, in alphabetical order, is a resumé of the Devon occurrences, excluding the present-day breeding colonies. We hope that this will stimulate people to visit those areas, for many of which there is no recent record, in order to establish the current status of the species in those localities.

**Ashcombe Copse** [ST2501], 1975 and 1976, S. Glover and N. Venn. **Ashclyst Forest** *[SY0099]*, July 10th 1983, P.S. Day; **Axmouth-Lyme Regis cliffs**, 1939, BRC, Monks Wood. **Aylesbeare and Harpford Commons** [SY0690], 1977, M.C. Robinson; 1981, I.D. Bullock.

**Beer Alston** *[SX4366]*, 1969-70 (Dev. Ass.). **Beggars Bush, near Chudleigh** *[SX8979]*, July 14th 1955, B.P. Braden (diaries). **Bickleigh Vale**, July 31st 1963, F.W. Jeffery. **Bovey Tracey**, July 1st 1946, S.T. Stidston; July 9th 1969, D.W. Mitchell [SX8078 and 8077], one at each spot (Dev. Ass.). **Branscombe (Hole)** [SY1989], 1970, DTNC. **Braunton** (Wright, 1932). **Bridford (east of)** [SX8286], 1985, W. Garforth. **Buckfastleigh Moor** *[SX6767]*, July 14th 1936, S.T. Stidston (Dev. Ass.). **Buckland in the Moor** *[SX7272]*, seven, July 13th 1970, D.W. Mitchell (Dev. Ass.); 1976, BRC, Monks Wood. **Burrator** *[SX5468]*, Aug. 1st 1960, F.W. Jeffery.

**Chillaton (Lee Farm)** [SX4483], Sept. 4th 1986, F.R. Philps. **Chulmleigh and Chawleigh area**, July; August 1969, only three, C.W.D. Gibson; 1976, C.W.D. Gibson (Dev. Ass.). **Clearbrook** *[SX5264]* July 28th 1963, F.W. Jeffery.

**Dawlish**, 1924, E.D. Morgan (Dev. Ass.); Stidston (1952). **Didworthy, near South Brent** [SX6862], July 13th and 14th 1989, M. Hazell.

**Eggesford (Flashdown Wood)** [SS6710], 1979, BRC, Monks Wood. **Eggesford (Hayne Valley)** [SS6610], July 5th 1985, K.C. Tyson. **Exeter (Stoke Woods)** [SX9396], Aug. 19th 1986, J.D. Leslie.

**Great Plantation, Heathfield**, July 3rd 1965 (one female), 'first seen for a number of years', L.H. Woollatt (Turner, 1966).

**Hackpen Hill, Hemyock** [ST1111], June 10th 1983, P.S. Day. **Hartland** [SS2225], July 2nd to 27th 1975, T. Jenkyn. **Hawkchurch** [ST3400], June 30th, July 31st 1973; 1978; Aug. 28th 1980, Aug. 11th 1982, K.A. Gosling. **Hawkswood, near Offwell** [SY2097], 1963 'a few'; 1967, 1970-73, 1975-79, J.R.W. Coxhead (Wallace, 1979). **Hennock (Reservoirs)** *[SX8082]*, 1954; 1956; 1958, C.W. Holcroft (RAMM). **Higher Metcombe** [SY0692], 1971 and July 26th 1985, G.H. Gush. **Huntsham** [ST0020], singleton, Aug. 24th 1990, R. Greenwood.

**Ilsington-Liverton**, 1950, 'extinct by 1962', A.H. Dobson (Dev. Ass.). **Inner Froward Point, Kingswear** [SX9049], July 2nd 1987, R. Tye. **Ivybridge** [SX6357], 1970, BRC, Monks Wood. **Kenton (Oxton)** *[SX9282]*, 1870-1904 (Studd diaries).

**Lynton (Lynbridge)** [SS7248], July 15th 1990, B. Chatfield.

**Mardon Down** [SX7686], July 25th 1987, R.C. Thornett. **Mile End, River Teign**, June 8th 1933, S.T. Stidston (Dev. Ass.). **Mitchelcombe**, July 27th 1963 (1 fresh), H.G. Hurrell (Dev. Ass.). **Mouth Mill to Clovelly** [SS2926], June 24th and Aug. 2nd 1974, T. Jenkyn.

**Newton Abbot (Aller Park Brake)** *[SX8769]*, 1975-79, R. Wood. **Newton Abbot (Bradley Wood)** *[SX8470]*, 1924, E.D. Morgan (Dev. Ass.); Stidston (1952). **Newton Abbot (Milber**

**Down)** *[SX8670]*, 1947 (Dev. Ass.), Stidston (1952). **North Brentor** [SX4981], July 1st 1986, S. Ford.

**Oakford** [SS8920], 1980, BRC, Monks Wood. **Old Mill Reserve** [SX8552], May 31st, June 2nd and Aug. 8th 1989, J. Bloomfield.

**Plympton (Newnham Park)** *[SX5557]*, 1950-55, R.G.H. (Dev. Ass.).

**Rifton** [SS8918], 1951, BRC, Monks Wood.

**Sidedown** [ST0100], 1980, BRC, Monks Wood. **Sidmouth**, June 13th 1957, B.F. Skinner (Dev. Ass.). **Southleigh** [SY2091], 1976, B. Henwood. **Southleigh (Records Cross)** [SY2091], up to 1979, A.J. Smart and B. Henwood (Wallace, 1979). **Southleigh (Wiscombe)** *[SY1893]*, 1970, T.J.C. Pearks (Dev. Ass.). **Southway** [SX6148], post-1960 (Plymouth BRC). **Spreacombe** *[SS4841]*, 1935, R.J. Burton (Stidston, 1952). **Stoke Hartland** [SS2324], June 22nd and July 13th 1974, T. Jenkyn. **Stoodleigh** *[SS9218]*, 1956 (Dev. Ass.). **Stover** [SX8375], Aug. 1st 1925 [not 1935] (Stidston, 1952); 1951, A.H. Dobson; June 26th 1976, D.W. Mitchell; 1980, BRC, Monks Wood.

**Tavy River** [SX5380], July 14th 1985, S. Ford. **Torquay (Chelston Cross)**, one, 1944, A.H. Dobson (Dev. Ass.). **Trenchford Reservoir**, 1958, C.W. Holcroft; July 1984, H.W. Eldridge; June 29th 1987, C. Cross. **Trusham** [SX8582], 1938, BRC, Monks Wood.

**Venn Ottery Common** [SY0692], 1971, BRC, Monks Wood. **Venn Ottery Common** [SY0691], 1976, G.H. Gush.

**Watersmeet, Lynmouth** [SS7448], July 4th 1985, S.D. Bruce. **West Down, Shaugh Prior** [SX5463], 1986, O.G. Watkins. **Whitland Cliff landslip** [SY3090], June 17th 1964 (Wallace, 1979). **Wonham, near Oakford** *[SS9221]*, 1956 (Dev. Ass.).

**Yard Moor, Ponsworthy** [SX6975], July 1986, G. Weymouth. **Youlston Wood, near Barnstaple** [SS6035-6036], 1980; July 18th 1981, Q. Paynter.

The butterfly normally flies from mid- to end of June (June 8th in 1933, S.T. Stidston, but May 28th 1893 (Hinchcliff, 1893)) until mid-August (Aug. 28th 1980, 'very worn', K.M. Gosling; Sept. 4th 1986, F.R. Philps).

# Dark Green Fritillary *Argynnis aglaja* (L.)     Plates 14c, 14d

This is one of the three 'large' fritillaries, and is reliably distinguished from the other two by the fairly deep green and large silvery spots (not streaks as in the Silver-washed Fritillary) on the underside (but see remarks under High Brown Fritillary).

The larval foodplants are *Viola* species.

Stidston's (1952) comment that this species 'is most frequently met with on the coast, though erratic in appearance. Sparingly, though widely distributed on rough common land and moors' is still true.

The Dark Green Fritillary flies from mid-June until mid-August. The earliest and latest dates are respectively May 20th 1990 (T.D. Sleep) and Sept. 9th 1987 (S. Ford).

# Silver-washed Fritillary *Argynnis paphia* (L.)     Plates 14e, 14f

This is the commonest and most widely distributed of the fritillaries, though in any one area it is never found in such numbers, as for example, the Marsh, Pearl- and Small Pearl-bordered fritillaries. From the map, it is clear that there is a concentration of records around the fringe of Dartmoor, but with a fairly regular scatter across the rest of the county. It is a butterfly of open

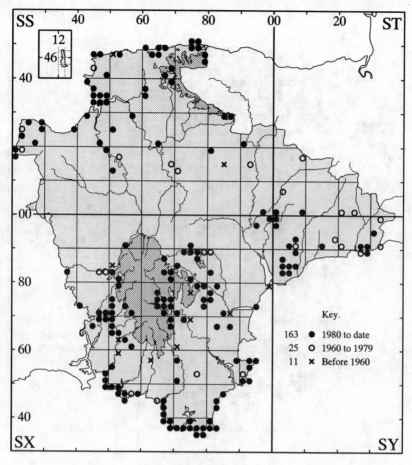

Dark Green Fritillary

woodlands and woodland edge, but it will wander some way from woods along hedgerows, and will happily come to Buddleia in village, or even town gardens.

The underside of both sexes is a faded green with silvery streaks. On the upperside, the male is distinguishable from the other two 'large' fritillaries by its 'rayed' appearance. Occasionally, a very dark form, *valezina*, of the female occurs.

The larval foodplants are various species of violet *Viola*.

The Silver-washed Fritillary flies from mid-July (occasionally late June; exceptionally May 27th, 1990, R. Khan) until the end of August, but sometimes to mid-September. The latest date is Oct. 2nd 1986 (E.W. Douglas).

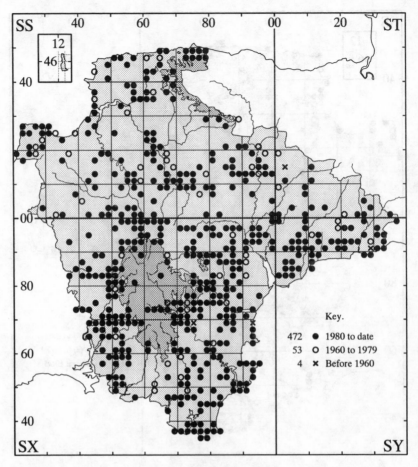

Key.

472  ● 1980 to date
53   ○ 1960 to 1979
4    ✗ Before 1960

Silver-washed Fritillary

## Marsh Fritillary *Eurodryas aurinia* (Rott.)          Plates 13e, 13f

Newman (1869) knew of only two sites in Devon (Exeter [probably Fordlands] (J. Hellins) and near Ivybridge (G.C. Bignell)), as localities of the Marsh or, as he knew it, Greasy Fritillary.

Parfitt (1878) regarded the Marsh Fritillary as local, but tolerably abundant, and thought that it was more restricted in its range than the Heath Fritillary. It was recorded from Axminster, Bideford, Dartmoor, Fordlands near Exeter, Ivybridge and Torquay. Barrett (1906) added Barnstaple, Instow and Torrington to the above, but noted that 'It has now disappeared from most of these places'.

Heath (1946, and manuscript additions) recorded the Marsh Fritillary at twenty three localities. Although Stidston's 1952 list was based on Heath (1946), few of Heath's localities were mentioned, but there were additional ones; there were eleven sites in total.

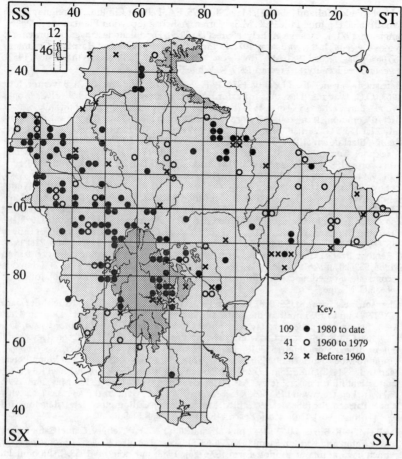

Key.

| | | |
|---|---|---|
| 109 | ● | 1980 to date |
| 41 | ○ | 1960 to 1979 |
| 32 | ✕ | Before 1960 |

Marsh Fritillary

Successive writers commented on the general increase of *aurinia* during the 1940s and early 1950s: 'common at Oakford' (Doe, 1942); 'after having been recorded as almost "extinct" in Devon, appears to be coming more common' (Bracken, 1943); 'very local, but apparently increasing' (Heath, 1946); 'still very local, but increasing' (Stidston, 1950); 'spreading throughout the county' (Stidston, 1951); 'thought to be increasing' (Stidston, 1952). At the present day, the Marsh Fritillary has been recorded on 109 tetrads since 1980, but several of these were singletons, and only about 90 tetrads supported colonies. Some colonies have died out in the last ten years, whilst some of the other 'spots' on the maps are based on introductions.

Below is set out all the known localities for the Marsh Fritillary. For many of the localities, only the date of the last sighting is given:

**Abbot's Park, Molland** [SS8027], May 29th 1975, E.C. Pelham-Clinton. **Ashreigney (High Wood)** [SS6311], June 14th 1980, M.S. Warren. **Ashclyst (Sprydon Plantation)** [SX9999], singleton, 1971, R.J. Clarke. **Ashclyst Forest** [SY0099]. Foodplant destroyed by spraying to remove 'weeds'; last record, May 1971, D. Pickering. **Aylesbeare and Harpford Commons** [SY0690] - last record 1981, M.C. Robinson. **Axminster** (not Exminster as in Stidston, 1952), a generalised locality; last record 1949, K. White (Dev. Ass.).

**Barnstaple**, a generalised locality, 1950, W.F. McCormick (Stidston, 1952). **Baventor**, June 1963, O.G. Watkins (Dev. Ass.). **Beaford Moor, Beaford** [SS5814], 1979 (BRC, Monks Wood). **Bere Ferrers** *[SX4463]*, 1942 (Bracken, 1943), 1946, 1965, O.G. Watkins (Dev. Ass.). **Bicton Common**, 'numerous but worn', May 20th 1956, B.F. Skinner (Dev. Ass.); singleton, July 21st 1985, G. Vernall. **Binworthy Moor, Welsford**, 1990; currently being drained, P. Rosser. **Blackdown Hills** *[ST0907]*. A small colony, 1978 and 1979, H.T. King (Dev. Ass.). **Blackpool Corner** [SY3398], up to 1973, K.M. White (Wallace, 1979). **Blagdon Moor, Holsworthy** [SS3404], June 4th 1968, W.H. Tucker. **Bottle Hill** [SX5561], July 8th 1967, F.W. Jeffery. **Bovey Heathfield**. In 1951, said to be increasing its range, A.H. Dobson (Dev. Ass.), but by 1969 'habitat was largely destroyed by fire' (Dobson, 1969). **Bovey Valley Woodlands** [SX7880], 1984, D.J. Hopkins. **Bower Moor, Bulkworthy** [SS3915], breeding colony, May 1992, W.H. Tucker. **Bradworthy Common, Bradworthy** [SS3214-3215]. A breeding colony. **Branscombe (Branscombe Undercliff)** *[SY1988]*, June 6th 1930 (Demuth, 1985:13). **Braunton Burrows** (Wright, 1932); 1967 (BRC, Monks Wood). **Brendon, and Thornbury** [SS3607 and 3707]. A breeding colony. **Brownsham, Mouth Mill** [SS2926], June 21st 1974, T. Jenkyn. **Brocks Common, near Germansweek** [SX4694]. A breeding colony. **Bursdon Moor** [SS2620 and 2619], colony, last record at first locality, June 4th 1977 (1 or 2), T. Jenkyn; second site, a breeding colony. **Burrow Cross, near Witheridge** [SS7616-7620], June 25th 1986, S.G. Madge.

**Chenson, near Lapford** [SS7008], June 4th 1963, W.H. Tucker. **Chudleigh Knighton Heath** *[SX8477]* - up to 1954 north of the heath, site subsequently ploughed, A.H. Dobson (Dev. Ass.). Specimen in the Torquay Museum is 'semi melanic', A.H. Dobson; 1984, D.J. Hopkins. **Chulmleigh and Chawleigh area**, last record 1976, C.W.D. Gibson (Dev. Ass.). **Coleford, near Stoodleigh** *[SS9019]*, 1951 and 1952, J. Harvey (G.M. Spooner, *pers. commn.*). **Common Moor, Hollocombe** [SS3601], 1979 (BRC, Monks Wood). **Common Moor, Peters Marland** [SS4412], June 25th 1972, W.H. Tucker. **Cookbury** *[SS4006]*, last seen July 1969, 'quite plentiful on moors' (Dev. Ass.). **Cookworthy** [SS4101], singleton May 26th 1990, W.H. Tucker. **Cornwood** *[SX6058]*, last record 1969, A.P. Gainsford (Dev. Ass.). **Cowley Wood, Parracombe** [SS6444], 1972 (BRC, Monks Wood). **Cullompton** - latest date June 3rd 1966 (Turner, 1967). **Culmstock Beacon** [ST1115], 1978, R.D. Sutton.

**DARTMOOR: Burrator** *[SX5468]*, June 8th and 30th 1957, F.W. Jeffery. **Cator (Cator Court, Lower Cator, and Riddon Farm)** [SX6776-6876]. Several small colonies, but some recently extinct. Two adults at Riddon Farm [SX6776], 1988, but none in 1989, J. Bloomfield. **Chagford (Higher Shapley Farm)** [SX6884], breeding colony 1992, N. Baldock. **Corndon Farm** [SX6974], May 23rd 1989, several males, J. Bloomfield. **Dartmeet (above)**, 1949, S.T. Stidston (Dev. Ass.). **Dart Valley, Holne** [SX7070], May 21st 1988, M.R. Hughes. **Dunsford Reserve and Steps Bridge, Dunsford** *[SX8088]*, last record 1971, R. Palmer (Dev. Ass.). **East Webburn River (Pudsham Down)** ?*[SX7174]*, only record June 18th 1961, H.A. Kennard. **Estrayer Park Farm, Okehampton** [SX5794], breeding colony 1992, N. Baldock. **Fernworthy** [SX6684], no date. **Hennock (Reservoirs)** *[SX8082]*, 1955, 1957, C.W. Holcroft (RAMM). **Horrabridge** [SX5169], July 8th 1967 (BRC, Monks Wood). **Mary Tavy (Burnford Farm)** [SX4979], June 19th 1983, T.D. Sleep. **Mary Tavy (Hill Bridge to Mary Tavy)** [SX5179-5380], 22nd June 1992. Several batches of eggs, K. Bastow. **Marystow (near)** *[SX4983]* - only record 1970 (Dev. Ass.). **Meldon Reservoir, Okehampton** [SX5590], 2 colonies 100m apart, June 10th 1984, E. Hart. **Moretonhampstead**, only record June 4th 1965, P.N. Crow (Dev. Ass.). **New Bridge, Holne** [SX7170], 1951 and 1952, G.M. Spooner. **New Park Waste**, 1935, H.G. Hurrell (Heath, 1946). **North Bovey (Youldon Farm)** [SX7384], breeding colony 1992, N. Baldock. **Padley Common, Chagford** [SX6987], caterpillars present 3rd May 1992, S.H. Mitchell. **Peter Tavy** *[SX5279]*, 1970 (Dev. Ass.). **Ponsworthy** [SX7074], 'abundant in 1984', G. Weymouth. **Postbridge**. Several small colonies. **Postbridge (Lych Way)** [SX6678 and 6778], July 1984, P.F. Goodfellow. **Postbridge (Runnage-Pizwell)** [SX6678], June 18th 1988, P.F. Goodfellow. **Sampford Spiney (Eggworthy)** [SX5471], June 10th 1985; June 14th 1986, S. Ford. **Sampford Spiney (Ward Bridge)** [SX5472], June 7th 1980, M.S. Warren. **Sampford Spiney (Withill Farm)** [SX5472], June 10th 1985, S. Ford, 2 adults June 19th 1988, but none in 1989, J. Bloomfield. **Sourton, Okehampton** [SX5389], May 1985, E. Hart. **Soussons** [SX6880], June 15th 1985, J.& J. Jones.

**Spitchwick, Holne** [SX7072], May 28th 1950, S.E. Moore. **Sticklepath** [SX6394], August 1957 (BRC, Monks Wood). **Swincombe Foot (near)** [SX6473], June 5th 1954, G.M. Spooner. **Thornworthy** [SX6785], breeding colony 1992, R. Waller. **Throwleigh (Clannaborough Farm)** [SX6691], strong colony, May 25th 1990, D.E. Bolton, B.J. Meloy, G. Musker. **Walkhampton** *[SX5571]*, last record June 25th 1950, F.W. Jeffery (Stidston, 1952). **Walla Brook** [SX6678], June 18th 1988, P. Goodfellow. **West Webburn River**, July 4th 1987, D.E. Bolton. **Whiddon Down (near)** [SX6890], July 1st 1986, S.G. Madge. **Widecombe**, S. Kemp (Heath, 1946); 1950 (Stidston, 1952). **Widecombe (Broadaford Farm)** [SX6977], breeding colony 1992, N. Baldock. **Yard Moor, Ponsworthy** [SX6974], June 26th 1985, 'Not as many as usual', G. Weymouth; approximately 8 adults, June 13th 1988, J. Bloomfield.

**Dawlish.** Numbers down to two males in 1902 (Rogers, 1903). **Deptford Moor and Farm** [SS2718 and 2717], existing colony. **Doves Moor, Stibb Cross** [SS4114], breeding colony, May 1992, W.H. Tucker. **Dunsdon Farm** [SS2907], one worn specimen, June 25th 1988, H. Marshall. **Dunsdon Farm NNR** [SS2806-08]. Breeding colonies, K. Bastow. **Dunstrear Moor** [SS5012], May 26th 1957, W.H. Tucker.

**East Youlstone** [SS2815]. A breeding colony. **East Youlstone (Hardsworthy, south of)** [SS2915]. A breeding colony, P. Rosser. **Eggesford, near Chulmleigh**, 1932 (Palmer, 1946). **Exeter (Beacon Heath)** [SX9494], singleton, May 29th 1982, R.J. Clarke. **Exeter (Pinhoe)** [SX9595], singleton, 1970s, R.J. Clarke.

**Fernhills Moor, near Samford Courtenay** [SX6399]. Site discovered June 1985, K. Tyson. **Fordlands** *[SX8690]*. Colony discovered June 1856 (Parfitt, 1856); last date - 1920.

**Germansweek** *[SX4493 - 4494]*, 1970 (Dev. Ass.). **Sampford Courtenay (Gilmoor)** [SX6399], June 24th 1984, G.M. Spooner. **Furley (Godworthy Bottom)** [ST2604], 1947 to c.1958, T.J. Wallace (Wallace, 1979). **Great Torrington** [SS4819], breeding colony 1991, J. Barrett.

**Haldon** [SX8784]. Between 6 and 10, June 18th 1988, D. Smallshire. **Harbertonford** [SX7755]. Small colony (of Witheridge Moor stock) introduced November 1987. Colony reinforced with larvae from Roadford in 1988. **Hares Down** [SS8320-8531]. Comprising Knowstone Inner Moor, Knowstone Outer Moor, and Rackenford Moor. Several breeding colonies in 1992. **Hartland Abbey, Hartland** [SS2426], June 1988, A. Fraser. **Hartland Forest, Welsford** *[SS2720]* (Jenkyn, 1968); two, July 10th 1987, R.J. Heckford. **Hartland Point** [SS2226], June 15th 1957, G.M. Spooner. **Hartland Quay (St Catherine's Tor)** [SS2224], June 18th 1958, July 8th 1963, T. Jenkyn. **Hatherleigh Moor** [SS5403], June 22nd 1981, T. Jenkyn. **Hawkchurch** [ST3400]. Singletons, June 1st 1973, 1976, K.A. Gosling. **Hawkswood, Offwell** *[SY2097]*, common up to 1978, none in 1979, J.R.W. Coxhead (Dev. Ass.). **Hemyock** [ST1313], singleton, 1985, E. Mallinson. **Hendon Moor** [SS2619], breeding colony 1992, P. Rosser. **Hendon Moor (East Bursdon Farm)** [SS2618], breeding colony 1991, P. Rosser. **Hense Moor, Luppitt** [ST1606], June 8th 1964, W.H. Tucker. **Highampton** [SS4902]. A breeding colony. **Highampton** [SS4703], last record May 29th 1977, T. Jenkyn. The site has deteriorated in the last few years. Devil's-bit Scabious present in small numbers, but is being crowded out. **Higher Metcombe** [SY0692], 1971; 1972 (BRC, Monks Wood). **Hittisleigh (near)** [SX7496], June 18th 1986, June 10th 1988, S.G. Madge. **Hollow Moor, Highampton** [SS4700-4701], last date June 19th 1986. **Holsworthy** [SS3304 - 3402] - 'quite plentiful', July 1969, G.E.C. Waterhouse. **Huddisford (Marshall Farm)** [SS3118]. A breeding colony, B. Martin; P. Rosser. **Huddisford Moor, Huddisford** [SS3119], breeding colony 1992, P. Rosser. **Huntshaw Woods, near Great Torrington** [SS4922], breeding colony, April 1992, W.H. Tucker.

**Ilfracombe (Warnscombe Farm)** *[SS5345]*. Specimens in Ilfracombe Museum dated June 16th 1930, May 1931 and June 8th 1932. Described as 'super abundant', June 15th 1931, but not so common since (Doe, 1941). **Instow-Barnstaple**, May 29th 1898, June 4-7th 1906, Studd Colln. (RAMM). **Ivybridge**, June 1889 (HEC, ex-colls. Meldola and Rowland-Brown).

**Kingford Fen, Pancrasweek** [SS2806], discovered in 1987 by K. Bastow, now an SSSI, but lack of grazing since 1988 has resulted in the site becoming overgrown, and Devil's-bit Scabious becoming crowded out, K. Bastow. **Kingsbridge** (Fox, 1874). **King's Nympton (1km NE of)** [SS6919], June 11th 1974 (BRC, Monks Wood).

**Lapford**, June 1942, W.E. Minnion, 'commonest fritillary' (Bracken, 1943). **Laughter Hole (near)** [SX6575], 2 worn specimens, July 21st 1986, G. Flower. **Liverton** [SX8175], c.1960 (BRC, Monks Wood). **Loddiswell (Andrew's Wood)** [SX7050]. An introduced colony (June 1968 the first date that we have, D.W. Mitchell). Two specimens, 1988, G. Waterhouse. **Lower Washfield, near Tiverton** [SS9416]. Small colony reinforced with stock from

Witheridge. **Luckett Moor** [SS8523], May 24th 1987, D.E. Bolton. **Luckroft, Northlew** [SS4700], May 26th 1988, J. Heath. **Lydford** [SX5084 and 4783-5083], last date 1972 (Plymouth BRC).

**Maiden Down, Culmstock,** last date 1978 (BRC, Monks Wood). **Mardon Down (Northmoor Bog)** [SX7587], June 21st 1987, D.E. Bolton. **Marsland RSNC Reserve** [SS2117], breeding colony 1990, G. Pilkington. **Meddon (near Deptford Farm)** [SS2718], breeding colony 1991, P. Rosser. **Melbury Wood, Powler's Piece** [SS3619-3720]. Last seen June 2nd 1985, I.D. Page. Possibly extinct due to timber felling. **Mortehoe** *[SS4444]*, 1903, 1905, 1906 'quite abundant in a very restricted area' (Longstaff, 1907b). Specimens from Boro' Valley, Mortehoe (May 26th, 1905) and Mortehoe (May 25th, 1909) caught by Longstaff, in HEC.

**Newcourt Wood, Sheepwash** [SS4907], breeding colony, June 1992, W.H. Tucker. **Newton Abbot (Decoy)** *[SX8670]*, no date, E.D. Morgan (Dev. Ass.). **Northleigh** *[SY1894]*, 'common', June 1966, J.R.W. Coxhead (Dev. Ass.). **Northlew (Scabsbury Copse)** [SS5101], June 6th 1988, J. Heath. **North Brentor** [SX4982], 1980-83, M.S. Warren. **North Tawton** *[SS6600]*, F.W. Jeffery (Heath, 1946).

**Oakford** [SS8920-9320], last date 1986, D.& H. Land. **Okehampton Castle** *[SX5894]*, 1970, J.C.A. Craik (Dev. Ass.), June 1987, G.A. Vaughan.

**Pancrasweek (Wooda Farm)** [SS3009], March 1992. Small colony, K. Bastow & S. Brown. **Paignton (Paignton Reservoir)** *[SX8661]*, July 12th 1935 (Stidston, 1952). **Perridge House, Ide, Exeter** *[SX8690]*, 1920, E.D. Morgan (Dev. Ass.). **Powler's Piece** [SS3718], last date 1979 (BRC, Monks Wood) - see also Melbury Wood.

**Rackenford Moor** - see Hares Down. **Roadford Reservoir** [SX4292]. A former colony, mostly destroyed by flooding. Some larvae taken to Harbertonford in 1988 by A.R. Hawtin. Small colonies existing around edges of reservoir April 1990, but threatened due to lack of management, K. Bastow. One good breeding colony in 1992, K. Spalding.

**Sampford Courtenay (near)** [SX6298], June 19th 1986, S.G. Madge. **Sidcombe**, May 20th 1948 (Dev. Ass.). **Sidmouth**. One taken in 1888 (Majendie, 1891). **Sillick Moor, Holsworthy** [SS3400]. A breeding colony, B. Martin; P. Rosser. **Southleigh** [SY2091]. A small colony. The land is burnt every few years which tends to decimate numbers, and the colony is vulnerable, B. Henwood. This is the last colony of the Marsh Fritillary in the 100km square SY. **Southleigh (Records Cross)** [SY2091], most years up to 1979, A.H.J. Smart and B. Henwood (Wallace, 1979), but no recent recording in this area. **Southmoor, Inwardleigh** [SS5600], June 6th 1985, W.H. Tucker. **Speke's Mill Bottom, Hartland** *[SS2223]*, last date 1960, P.N. Crow (Dev. Ass.). **Springhead** [SY2790], 1973, T.J. Wallace (Wallace, 1979).

**Tamar Valley** [SS2810-12], 1989, but site management required to improve conditions, K. Bastow. **Tavistock**, June 4th 1965, P.N. Crow (Dev. Ass.). **Thorndon** [SX5192], June 14th 1988, J. Heath. **Thorne Moor** [SS4014-4116], 1990. Strong colony, K. Bastow. **Thrushell River** [SX5292], 1988, J. Heath. **Tiverton-Halberton**, June 2nd 1955, 'quite common', G.R.M. (Dev. Ass.). **Torquay**, Parfitt (1878) and J. Walker (Heath, 1946).

**Upcott, near Germansweek** [SS4396]. A breeding colony, B. Martin; P. Rosser. **Upcott Farm, near Holsworthy** [SS3705]. A breeding colony, B. Martin; P. Rosser.

**Venn Down, near Thorndon Cross** [SX5095], June 14th 1988, J. Heath. **Venn Mills (East Putford)** [SS3918], existing colony, J. Rosser. **Venn Ottery Common** [SY0691]. Died out, for no obvious reason in 1979, G.H. Gush. Singleton, dead, July 12th 1986, R.H. Newland.

**Waterhouse** [SX5198], May 19th 1988, J. Heath. **Welcombe** [SS22-24 17-18], first locality, July 9th and 11th 1967, T.P. (Dev. Ass.); second locality, 1990, P. Rosser. **Welsford Moor** [SS2720], a breeding colony, P. Rosser. **Wester New Moor** [SS8225], May 24th 1987, D.E. Bolton. **Whiteleigh Meadow** [SS4102], breeding colony, June 1992, W.H. Tucker. **Wiston Moor** [SS8224], May 24th, 1987, D.E. Bolton. **Witheridge Moor**. Probably the county's stronghold. **Withleigh, Buzzards** [SS9011], June 1972, D. Pickering. **Wolf River, E. Grinnacombe-Hennard Jefford, =Roadford** [SX4292], June 23rd 1987, D.E. Bolton. **Woodbury Common** [SY0286], last date, June 14th 1956, B.F. Skinner (Dev. Ass.). **Woodford Bridge, Westward Ho!** *[SS4228]*, 1893, E.M. Eustace (Dev. Ass.). **Woolfardisworthy (Kennerland Farm)** [SS3322], breeding colony 1992, P. Rosser. **Woolfardisworthy (Higher West Town Farm)** [SS3220], breeding colony 1991, P. Rosser. **Wotter, Shaugh Prior** *[SX5561]*, June 1950, 1951 and 1959, P. Jeffery.

**Yarcombe** [ST20], 1970 (BRC, Monks Wood).

The Marsh Fritillary normally normally flies from the end of May (April 27th 1893 (Hinchcliff, 1893)); May 6th 1938 (Watkins, 1938) until about the third week in June, but occasionally until early July (July 24th 1976, G.H. Gush).

## Glanville Fritillary *Melitaea cinxia* (Linnaeus)

Reading (1862) stated that this was a species 'reputed to occur in the district', but 'no positive evidence of its capture'.

## Heath Fritillary *Mellicta athalia* (Rottemburg)                 Plate 15c

Nationally, the Heath Fritillary has declined dramatically during the last 100 years. Today, it only occurs in restricted colonies in Cornwall, Somerset, Devon and Kent, with introduced colonies in Essex. It is usually associated with open patches of woodland, particularly areas regenerating after coppicing. Less commonly in Devon, it occurs on unimproved plantain-rich grasslands and sheltered heathland slopes. The national contraction in range is thought to be related to the decline in coppicing.

### Current distribution

The Heath Fritillary was once widespread in Devon, the Country's former stronghold. It now only occurs in three areas in the county, at only one of which does its future look secure.

In the first area, north of Tiverton, the several small fragmented colonies are all vulnerable unless active conservation measures can be undertaken. Of six sites known at the beginning of the 1980s, only two or three remain. The colonies, which occurred over a 4-km tract, appear to have been generally fairly small, although 200-300 adults were present at some sites (Warren, *pers. commn.*). Most were in abandoned hay meadows that were planted with conifers, hence their rapid decline. *M. athalia* was occasionally able to survive for short periods in clear-felled and newly planted areas. As the woodland developed, so the colonies declined and became extinct. Some colonies survived in herb-rich meadows, but these were subject to bracken and scrub invasion. Clearance by the owner of one such site [not intended for the butterflies well being], combined with heavy grazing, destroyed a superb colony (estimated population of 550 in 1986; none seen in 1987). However, not all is quite lost, as the owner of another site is allowing some management by Butterfly Conservation. Eighteen adults were seen on a rainy day in early June 1990 (R.D. Sutton); a pair under dull conditions, June 17th 1990 (C.R. Bristow). Only 3 adults were seen on June 17th 1991 (R.D. Sutton); 10 seen June 11th 1992 (R.D. Sutton, A. Liebert).

In a second area, in West Devon, which appears to have been recolonised in 1985, positive steps towards its conservation are being undertaken by the sympathetic owners, but numbers remain very low (only 2 adults seen, May 31st 1990 (A. Mackonochie); none seen June 6th (T.D. Sleep); only one seen on June 17th 1991 (A. Mackonochie)).

119

The status of the two colonies in the third, moorland, area on the Devon part of Exmoor, which were only discovered in 1987, seems to be fairly secure. Some 30-40 adults were seen on one occasion in 1988, and others were seen by B. Henwood and M.& B. Blackmore on June 15th and 16th. In 1989, predicted adult numbers at the peak flight period at these colonies were 131 and 285 (M.S. Warren, *pers. commn.*). In 1991, D.J. Land saw 25-30 in a half-hour period on July 4th.

Below are all the former colonies and sightings in Devon:

**Ashreigney (Ash Wood)** *[SS6214]*, June 16th 1940; July 2nd 1941; June 15th 1942; July 30th 1943; June 21st 1949, R.G.H.; July 24th 1961, A.H. Dobson (Dev. Ass.). None seen July 9th 1972, J. Thomas and R.M. Pyle, but Cow-wheat abundant in a young, low conifer plantation. Area not visited recently. See also Hodgson Wood, Densham.

**Barnstaple**. Mathew (1858b) caught 26 in a wood 'near Barnstaple' in June 1858. Probably the basis of the records in Parfitt (1878) and Barrett (1906). **Bere Ferrers**, June 13th 1965, R.J. Revell (Dev. Ass.). **Bickleigh (Shaugh Bridge)** (Reading, 1862). **Bickleigh Vale**, June 1857, *'athalia* in abundance' (Lethbridge, 1857); 2, May 31st 1858 (Dell, 1858); April 1865 'found feeding a colony of *Melitaea athalia* in same spot as last year - full fed'; May 1865 'brought home from Plymbridge about 50 larvae - *Melitaea athalia* - fully fed' (G.C. Bignell, notebook in Plymouth Museum); - probably the 'above Plymbridge' of Reading (1862), and the 'near Plymouth' of Basden Smith (1894), where they were 'plentiful in one locality'. **Blanchdown Wood**. 1942, G.M. Spooner; 1960s (M. Warren, *pers. commn.*). **Bridestowe**, one, A. Druitt (Heath, 1946). **Buckland Woods** (Jordan, 1842).

**Chagford**, 1910, S.T. Stidston (Dev. Ass.). **Chulmleigh (near)**, five, June 19th 1960, A.H. Dobson (Dev. Ass.). **Codden Hill, Bishop's Tawton** [SS5829]. Discovered June 1973 by T. Jenkyn when over 50 adults seen. In 1974, about 12 adults were recorded; 'a few' in 1976, but none between 1977 and 1982. However, in 1983, a few adults were observed, and on June 25th 1984, 7 were recorded in 35 minutes, to give an estimated population of 34, M.S. Warren. Visits by K. Bastow and D. Smallshire in 1988, yielded no Heath Fritillary, A two-hour visit by D. Smallshire on June 25th 1989 also revealed no Heath Fritillary. The habitat now looks most unsuitable because of domination by gorse, bracken and birch, although Cow-wheat occurs along the narrow paths. None was seen during a 60-minute search by M. Warren on June 14th 1989.

**Dartmeet**, A. Simmons, June 1904 (Dev. Ass.). **Dawlish (near)**, 1898, 'in hundreds; taken since, but not in such numbers' (Mayor, 1919).

**Eggesford, near Chulmleigh**, 1934 (Burton, 1944), 1957 and 1960, H.A. Kennard; four, June 24th 1961, A.H. Dobson; 'Disappeared by 1967', H.A. Kennard (Turner, 1968). **Erme River**, two, 1902, S.T. Stidston (Dev. Ass.). **Exeter** - probably Fordlands of the older literature. **Exmoor** (Barrett, 1906); June 10th and 24th 1956, G. Maunders (Dev. Ass.)

**Fordlands** *[SX8690]*. Discovered June 1856 (Parfitt, 1856). 'Formerly in Fordlands Woods' (Barrett, 1906).

**Great Consols Mine, Tamar Valley** *[SX4273]*. Discovered by S. Kemp in 1941; 2 seen (1 taken) June 4th 1942 (G.M. Spooner, *pers. commn.*). **Gunnislake (Devon side of Tamar)** [SX4270], in clearings made for anglers, 1940, O.G. Watkins.

**Haldon Hill**, Col. Donovan (Heath, 1946). **Hodgson Wood, Densham** [SS6412], 1962, ?1970 (Monks Wood, BRC). **Hollocombe (near)**, June 23rd 1962 (possibly Narracott or Hodgson Wood) (Monks Wood, BRC). **Horrabridge** (Barrett, 1906).

**Instow** (Barrett, 1906). **Ivybridge** (Reading, 1862; Parfitt, 1878).

**Jennett's Reservoir (top end)**, 1947, G.H. Gush; planted with conifers after 1947.

**Kingsbridge** (Reading, 1862). **Knowstone** [SS8222], June 3rd 1980 (BRC, Monks Wood). Record not verified, possibly a misidentified Marsh Fritillary.

**Lapford (near)** [=?Eggesford], June 7th 1937, Major Gay (Doe, 1941); 1943, W.E. Minnion (Heath, 1946). **Lee ['Leigh'] [=Borough] Valley, Ilfracombe**, Aug. 28th 1928 (Bell, 1933). The late date is most unusual (but see Harvie, 1866); 3 of the 6 specimens were fresh, suggesting to Bell that they were a partial second brood. More likely, these were not Heath Fritillaries, but some other small fritillary, since Bell (1933:108) also recorded the 'Heath'

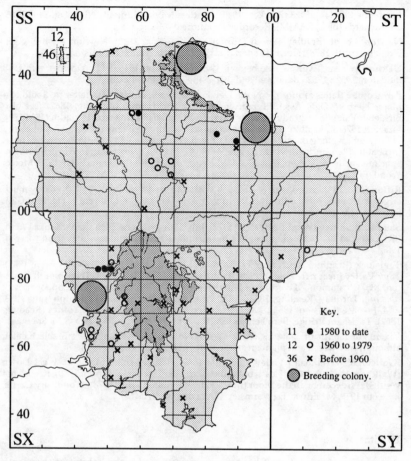

SS     40       60       80      00      20    ST

Key.

11  ●  1980 to date
12  ○  1960 to 1979
36  ✗  Before 1960

⬤ Breeding colony.

SX                                      SY

## Heath Fritillary

Fritillary at Swanage in Dorset, an area where they have been recorded neither previously nor since (Thomas and Webb, 1984). The Small Pearl-bordered Fritillary is an obvious candidate, as Bell had seen one worn specimen earlier in the day, but as he stated that 'we at first mistook them [i.e. *athalia*] for *selene*', it would appear to rule out the latter species. A more likely species is the Marsh Fritillary as it used to be common near the Borough Valley, and has been recorded near Swanage. However, like *athalia*, *aurinia* has not previously been recorded as late as the end of August. Their true identity will probably never be known. **Leigh Moor (Dartmoor Tramway)** (Reading, 1862). **Lydford (Lyd Valley)**, 'only a mile from the railway site', 1941-43, R.C.L. Perkins (via G.M. Spooner). **Lydford (old railway)**. First seen in 1969. In 1970, the following numbers were recorded: June 9th (43), June 20th (81), and July 9th (20), C.J.A. Craik (Dev. Ass.). About 800 were seen in two hours in 1972 [SX4983]; in 1973 and 1974, over 100 adults per hour were counted. Thereafter, numbers declined; there were scattered groups in 1975. Heavy commercial collecting occurred during the late 1970s. In 1978, 17 adults per hour were seen [SX4682]; a few were seen along the nature trail in Lydford Forest. There were also a few sightings along the nature trail and in Coryhill Plantation in 1979. By 1980, much of the railway line was overgrown and only 2 adults seen; none in 1981-1983 despite frequent visits (Warren, 1985). In 1984, a singleton was observed. A singleton possibly seen in 1987. None seen by T. Sleep on May 27th and June 15th 1988 - the whole area badly overgrown.

**Mortehoe** [SS4444], 1928 (Bracken, 1940). **Mutters Moor, Sidmouth** [SY1088], 1950-1966, T.J. Richards (BRC, RAMM). Record not confirmed.

**Newton Abbot (Bradley Wood)** (Turton and Kingston, 1830). **Newton Bushel**, Capt. Blomer (Parfitt, 1878). **North Tawton (near)**, 1943, W.E. Minnion (Stidston, 1952).

**Oakford** [='near Tiverton', see below], 1945, O.D. Hunt; 1948, W.H. Dowdeswell; 1948 (Stidston, 1952); 1952, 'done well and increasing' (Stidston, 1952b).

**Parracombe (lanes around)**, = North Devon locality of South (1892) (letter by South to a Major Herbert, Dev. Ass.). **Plymbridge (above and below)** (Reading, 1862) (see also Bickleigh Vale). 15 to 20 adults on the old railway, and 6 near the second viaduct [SX5160], June 6th 1976, K. Mutton (2 taken and in his collection). Area now overgrown, but plenty of Cow-wheat along the old railway (T.D. Sleep, *pers. commn.*). **Plymouth**, 'abundant near' [probably Plymbridge and Bickleigh Vale], G. Bignell (Newman, 1869). **Princetown**. Specimen in the A. Tonge Colln., Booth Museum, dated 1901 (Luckens, 1980); 1939 (Monks Wood, BRC).

**Rifton** *[SS8918]* [=Stoodleigh of Blundell's School], June 1949 (worn); 1950, colony much larger, common, June 26th, over by July 2nd, J. Harvey; 1951, seven, J. Harvey (G.M. Spooner, *pers. commn.*).

**Sampford Spiney (Ward Bridge)** [SX5472], July 15th 1972, one, F. Brahan (Monks Wood, BRC). Record not verified, possibly a misidentified Marsh Fritillary. **Staverton** (Barrett, 1906).

**Tavistock** (Reading, 1862); near Tavistock, S. Kemp (Heath, 1946); 1960 (Warren, 1985). **Tavy Valley (near rifle range)**, 1920s, P.N. Crow (via G.M. Spooner). **Teignmouth** (Stainton, 1857), 'common'. **'Tiverton'** of Blundell's School = Oakford area (G.M. Spooner, *pers. commn.*). **Torquay** (Reading, 1862); 1902, W. Crocker (Dev. Ass.). **Torrington**, June 1893, E.M. Eustace (Stidston, 1952); 1906, H. Doidge (Studd Colln., RAMM). **Totnes** (Reading, 1862). **Tuckham Bridge, Bere Ferrers** [SX4464], one, R.J. Revell, 1965 (via G.M. Spooner).

**Vixen Tor (south of)**, late 1960s, D. Wedd. Now (1988) no longer a suitable habitat, although cow-wheat and plantain are present (T.D. Sleep, *pers. commn.*).

**'Wallcomb'** [?Walkham] Valley, June 21st 1889 (HEC, ex-colln. Meldola). **West Down (Walkham Valley)**, 1979, 'Heath butterflies seen', O.B. Morton (Warren, 1980). Record not verified. **Widecombe in the Moor (near)**, R. Hall Jordan (Parfitt, 1878). **Woodbury Castle**, June 6th 1919, Mr Edwards (Warmsley-White diaries, RAMM).

## Habitat

Warren *et al.* (1984) list four main features for the habitat of the Heath Fritillary: 1. They occupy predominantly woodland habitats in an early stage of succession or regeneration. 2. These situations usually exist for only a few years in any one part of a wood. 3. Breeding areas are typically open and sunny. 4. Current sites are on nutrient-poor or acidic soils.

The existing colonies in Devon fall into three main types:

a). Newly planted coniferous woods, recently coppiced and clear-felled woodland - Common Cow-wheat *Melampyrum pratense* the sole foodplant.

b). Former hay meadows, or herb-rich grasslands - Narrow-leaved Plantain *Plantago lanceolata* and Germander Speedwell *Veronica chamaedrys* the main foodplants.

c). Sheltered valley sides on moorland - Cow-wheat, the main foodplant, with Foxglove *Digitalis purpurea* the secondary foodplant.

Most Devon Heath Fritillary sites fall into one or other of the above categories. For example, those along the old Lydford railway correspond to category 'a'; Codden Hill falls mostly in 'c', but some in 'b'. There are, however, significant differences between the first and last habitat types, and the middle one. In 'b', Narrow-leaved Plantain is the dominant larval foodplant, but Germander Speedwell is an important secondary foodplant, whereas on 'a' and 'c', Common Cow-wheat, which grows sparsely among the heathland vegetation, is the main foodplant. Additionally, the Foxglove is a secondary foodplant in 'c' (Warren, 1984; 1991). As well as the above foodplants, larvae, particularly spring larvae in years of exceptional abundance, have been recorded in Cornwall on Yarrow Milfoil *Achillea millefolium*, Wood Sage *Teucrium scorodonia* and Lesser Celandine *Ranunculus ficaria* (Gainsford, 1974; Warren *et al.*, 1984).

In woodland and grassland habitats, the larval foodplant is of secondary importance to the amount of shade. In old meadows which have been newly planted, and clear-felled areas of former deciduous woodland, Cow-wheat can abound; in abandoned meadows, railway cuttings etc. in Devon, Narrow-leaved Plantain is often common to abundant. In these situations, a rapid build up in numbers can occur (see Luckens, 1980), only to be followed by a rapid decline, or extinction, as the site deteriorates with the growth of the newly planted trees, or by scrub invasion (see the Lydford site above). At one of the Oakford sites, open conditions were maintained by annual removal of some trees for Christmas. The colony was discovered in 1972; peak numbers were in 1982 when the adult population was estimated at 485. Only 2 were seen in 1983. In 1984 and 1985, 21 and 30 respectively, were seen. Between 1 and 4 were seen in 30 minutes in 1986 (M. Warren, *pers. commn.*). None has been seen in the last six years. Thus, under artificial conditions, this colony survived for something like 14 years, whereas, the Lydford colony only lasted 10 years before being shaded out by natural regeneration - this compares with a 6-year (Luckens, 1980) or 4 to 6-year period (Warren, 1984) for colonies in coppiced Kentish woodland. Thus, most colonies in open woodland, regenerating woodland or abandoned meadows, without active conservation, are doomed to extinction. This suggests that prior to woodland management, the Heath Fritillary habitat was sheltered moorland valleys in which scrub, bracken and bramble growth was kept naturally in check by a combination of grazing and periodic burning. Such habitats presumably hold the key to the species' long-term survival.

## Conservation

Warren *et al.* (1984) concluded that, although the conservation of the Heath Fritillary through the establishment of nature reserves had been unsuccessful, recent management activities are more hopeful. *M. athalia* is not easy to conserve, especially on small reserves, because of the ephemeral nature of its breeding habitat and the need for intensive management. The rate at which a large colony can become established on a reserve is governed by the rate of immigration from neighbouring colonies.

### Re-establishment

The earliest documented attempt at introduction of the Heath Fritillary in Devon was by Warren in 1982 (Warren, 1985). Fifteen newly emerged adults and about 50 pupae of Cornish stock were introduced into a site on an old railway line. The pupae were placed on a wooden platform standing in a bowl of water to protect them from predators. Some adults were seen the following day, but the weather then became dull and wet for the next three weeks. During that time, all the pupae hatched, and a few adults were seen on subsequent visits. However, owing to the marginal suitability of the habitat, the long span of emergence and poor weather conditions, the attempt failed.

Warren (1985) noted that this site could be restored by scrub clearance. With the cooperation of the owner, the enthusiastic drive of Tom Sleep, the approval of 'officers of Butterfly Conservation' and the expert help of Martin Warren, clearance of this site began in November 1988 (Sleep, 1989). At the same time, the Forestry Commission began tree felling on two large areas of adjacent woodland, making in total a fine area for re-establishing the species.

### Variation in adult markings

Ford (1945b) noted the Heath Fritillary in the West Country differs from that in Kent by being slightly smaller and with more pointed wings, and the ground colour is rather duller and a less red tone. Luckens (1980) noted that the Heath Fritillary shows much individual variation, but thought that the Devon and Cornwall populations showed some consistent variations. West Country females occur in two different forms in roughly equal proportions. Both are smaller on average than Kentish females, but one is very similar, if not identical in general condition and pattern, to those in Kent. The other, however, tends to have rather contrasting yellow as well as reddish markings within the dark reticulate pattern. This latter pattern occurs only rarely in Kent. Possibly, this variation is related to the differing foodplants.

### Flight period

The Heath Fritillary has a restricted flight period, normally from mid-June to mid-July. Earliest date, May 31st (Dell, 1858), but with an exceptional (if genuine) April 27th (Hinchcliff, 1893); latest date, July 30th 1943. The August date of Bell (1933) is discussed above. There is one other Devon August date (Harvie, 1866). As Harvie was familiar with both the Pearl-bordered and Small Pearl-bordered fritillaries, he was not likely to confuse those species with the Heath Fritillary. It therefore seems possible that, occasionally, *athalia* flies in August.

# Satyridae

## Speckled Wood *Pararge aegeria* (Linnaeus)      Plate 15d

This is one of the most widespread of Devon's butterflies. It occurs along open rides in woodlands, along leafy lanes, hedgerows and gardens where there are patches of shade and light.

It is one of the earliest of the non-hibernating butterflies to appear and one of the last to disappear. It normally flies from the end of April until early October, but is not uncommon at the end of March (there are some February sightings) or early November. There have, however, been some exceptional sightings. In 1988/1989, N. Barns saw one in every month of the year, with singletons on Dec. 8th, Jan 23rd and February. In 1989, there were sightings from

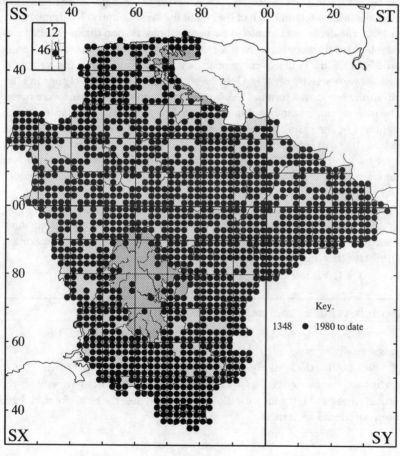

Speckled Wood

125

March 26th onwards. In 1990, it was first seen on March 10th (T.D. Sleep), with several sightings from March 17th onwards.

Spring temperatures influence the development rates of the overwintering larvae, normally 3rd instar, and pupae, resulting in a variable, but staggered spring emergence period.

The Speckled Wood is double brooded, with the second generation emerging at about the beginning of July; occasionally a third brood will appear at the end of September and may persist to mid-November.

The larval foodplants are grasses such as Couch-grass *Elymus repens*, Cock's-foot *Dactylis glomerata* and Annual Meadow-grass *Poa annua*.

## Wall *Lasiommata megera* (Linnaeus)                                   Plate 15e

This is one of the brightest of the 'browns' and could at first sight be mistaken for a fritillary. Normally, it is widespread throughout the county, but numbers in Devon (and much of the rest of the West Country) fell dramatically in 1983. The decline as chronicled by personal observation (Bristow, 1987) was corroborated by records received for the Provisional Atlases: up to the spring brood of 1983, the Wall was common in Devon, but in autumn of that year, only 7 adults were seen by Bristow. Only 2 were noted in 1984, and only one in 1985. No spring brood was seen in 1986, but 2 autumn brood specimens were noted. The increase that began in autumn 1986 continued in 1987. There were several sightings of the spring brood, and many more in the autumn (Bristow and Bolton, 1988); in 1988, numbers were almost back to normal, and in 1989, they were back to their pre-1983 level. In fact, 1989, which was an exceptional year for many species, was a very good year for the Wall - there were three broods and adults flew well into October.

The Wall is normally double brooded, with the first generation emerging in about mid-May, and the second about the beginning of August. Sometimes there is a third brood in October. The earliest and latest dates are respectively April 11th (Hinchcliff, 1893) and Nov. 13th (Mathew, 1916).

The larval foodplants include all the common grasses.

## Scotch Argus *Erebia aethiops* (Esper)

A specimen noted by Miss Tallant, and confirmed by a Mr Paul Henry, was seen all day in a garden at Ottery St Mary on July 15th 1944 (Stidston, 1949). It is possible that the butterfly was an aberration of the Meadow Brown *Maniola jurtina* ab. *excessa* Leeds (Russwurm, 1978) which superficially resembles the Scotch Argus. But if the identification was correct, then the butterfly must have been introduced accidentally.

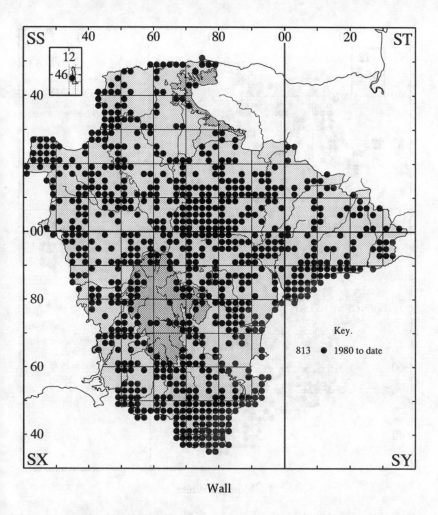

12
46

40

00

80

60

40

SX SY

Key.

813 ● 1980 to date

Wall

## Marbled White *Melanargia galathea* (Linnaeus)    Plate 15f

The Marbled White was one of the earliest butterflies to be recorded in Devon. Polwhele's (1797) reference to a 'curious Black and White butterfly in the woods at Lindridge' must refer to this species.

This is a distinctive, widespread species that probably occurs wherever its foodplants grow on ungrazed or lightly cut or cropped meadows, roadside verges etc. It is absent over the higher ground of Dartmoor.

Whilst frequently exploiting suitable linear habitats, e.g. motorway verges and railway embankments, colonies are often restricted to isolated sections within a larger run of apparently suitable habitat. In mid-Devon, many colonies are found on small areas of damp alluvial meadows.

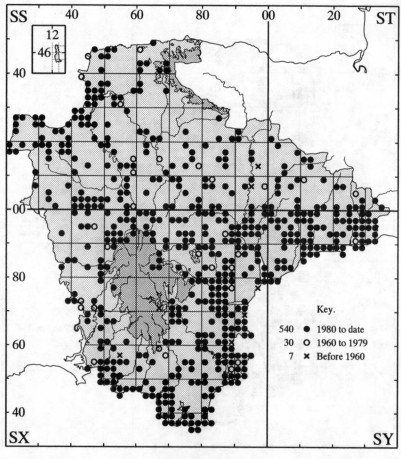

Marbled White

The larval foodplants are grasses, and include Cat's-tail *Phleum pratense*, Cock's-foot *Dactylis glomerata* and Sheep's-fescue *Festuca ovina*. The female does not oviposit in the normal manner, but drops her eggs in flight.

The flight period is normally July. The earliest date is June 8th (1962, F.W. Jeffery). Adults occasionally linger on into September (there were several September sightings in 1986). In October, it was recorded on the 4th in 1979 (Archer-Lock, 1979) and 5th in 1986 (M.J. Lee).

## Grayling *Hipparchia semele* (Linnaeus)                    Plate 16a

This is dominantly a species of moor and heathland. The distribution map shows that the Grayling occupies a broad band through the central southern part of the county, together with colonies along the north and south coasts. The largest colonies occur on the heaths in the east of the county, and on Braunton Burrows.

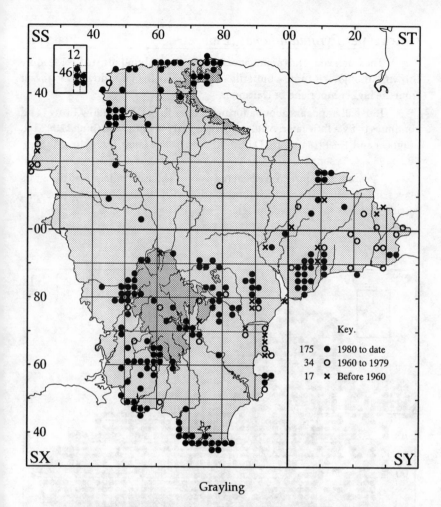

Grayling

It is good to report that, although not seen along the coast on either side of Tor Bay since 1976, it was seen again on Berry Head in 1986 (K. Tucker, N. Ward and J. Johnson). It has not been seen on the north side of Torbay (at Anstey's Cove) since 1976 (E.C. Pelham-Clinton). It is also now rarely recorded from the coast south of Hartland where it used to be common.

Whilst not a migrant, Graylings do occasionally wander and turn up in unexpected areas, ie. one at Budlake [SX9899] (possibly using the M5 as a dispersal route) in 1982 (C.R. Bristow) (see also Archer-Lock, 1979).

The larval foodplants are grasses such as Couch-grass *Elymus repens*, fescues, including Sheep's Fescue *Festuca ovina*, and Red Fescue *F. rubra*, Tufted Hair-grass *Deschampsia cespitosa* and Early Hair-grass *Aira praecox*.

The adults normally fly from mid-July to the first week of September. The earliest and latest dates are respectively June 14th (1990, P. Coombs) and Oct. 7th (1986, S. von Reibnitz).

## Gatekeeper *Pyronia tithonus* (Linnaeus)                    Plate 16b

The Gatekeeper has a similar distribution and abundance to the Meadow Brown, although it is more a butterfly of hedgerows than meadows. It is absent from the higher moorland of Dartmoor.

It usually appears about a fortnight later than the Meadow Brown and continues to fly a little later. Adults emerged early in both 1986 (June 12th, M.R. Hughes) and 1989 (May 28th, D.C.M. Radford). The latest flying time is Sept. 30th (1986, K. Tyson).

Eggs are laid in warm sheltered spots. The caterpillars feed on grass leaves of a variety of species including couch *Agropyron* spp., bents *Agrostis* spp., fescues *Festuca* spp. and meadow grass *Poa* spp.

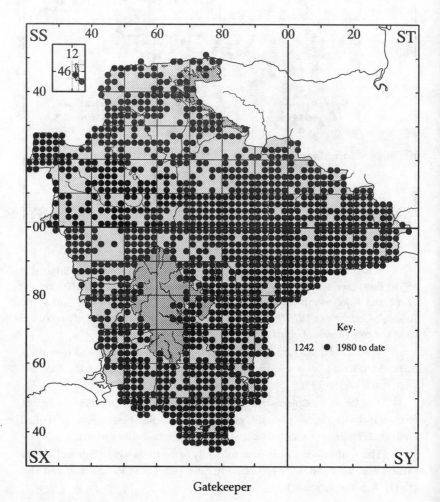

Gatekeeper

# Meadow Brown *Maniola jurtina* (Linnaeus)    Plate 16c

At the height of its flying period (mid-June to mid- or late August), this is probably the commonest butterfly in the county. It occurs in meadows, gardens, open rides in woodland, on verges etc. - anywhere where its larval foodplants, the grasses (especially species of *Poa*) grow.

The earliest date is May 12th (1945, F.W. Jeffery). In 1986, there were several October sightings up to the 16th (V.R. Tucker). The latest dates are, however, Oct. 31st 1979 and Nov. 2nd 1980 (Archer-Lock, 1980a; c).

Females in West Devon and Cornwall generally have more spots on the hindwing underside than those to the east and in southern England. Greenwood (1963) found that female Meadow Browns on Lundy had spotting which corresponded to that of southern England, and not to that of west Devon and Cornwall. In some years, the boundary between the two groups appears to be abrupt, even occurring between adjacent fields (Dowdeswell, 1981). The bound-

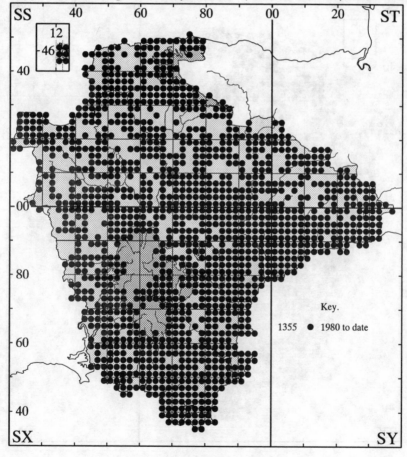

Meadow Brown

ary between the two types appears to move west or east, between generations. However, this shift is now thought to be more apparent than real, due to variation in the sampling time in relation to the flight period, interacting with the intra-season shifts in spotting, and also to environmental affects on spot numbers which can change from year to year.

## **Ringlet** *Aphantopus hyperantus* (Linnaeus)                Plate 16d

The Ringlet is common and widely distributed, but has been recorded on fewer tetrads than the Meadow Brown and Gatekeeper which share similar habitats, although the Ringlet is commonly associated with generally damper grasslands than the Meadow Brown. Larvae have been recorded on *Dactylis glomerata* in Devon. This may partly be due to under-recording because of its shorter flight period - normally July. It has been seen as early as May 25th, J. Kingsley-Smith. In 1986, there were a number of October sightings, ending Oct.

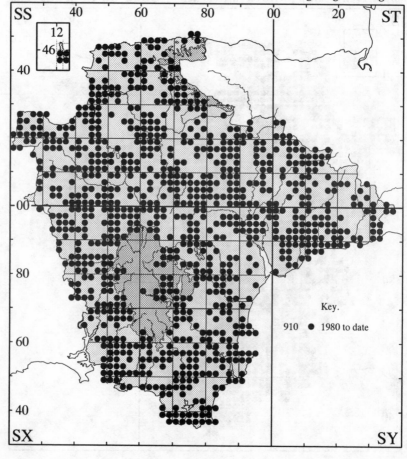

Ringlet

8th (J.M. Cook). Numbers fluctuate quite markedly - 1984 seemed a poor year, whereas 1985 - 1989 were much better.

The Ringlet is a very dark, chocolate-brown butterfly with a very fluttery flight. When fresh, the white fringes to the wings can be seen during flight, otherwise, the prominent ringlets on the underside of the wings are a sure guide to its identification.

## Small Heath *Coenonympha pamphilus* (Linnaeus)    Plate 16e

This is dominantly a species of moors and heaths, which is reflected in the distribution map. It is still found on the larger blocks of Culm grassland, but may have declined as this habitat has suffered considerable loss through drainage, ploughing etc. However, sowing of motorway and major road embankments and cuttings with mixed fine-leaved grasses has encouraged the spread of the Small Heath into these new habitats.

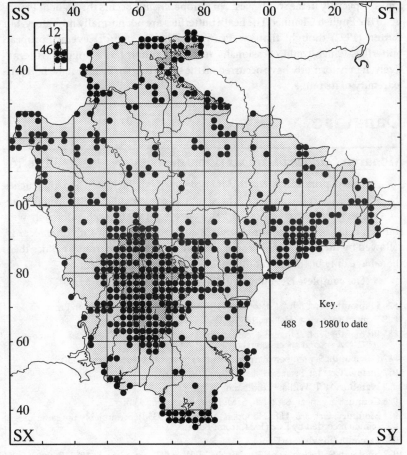

Small Heath

The Small Heath is double brooded, with the first generation emerging in late May (earliest date, April 27th 1893 (Hinchcliff, 1893)), or early June, and the second generation in mid- to late August or early September (latest date, Oct. 13th, T.D. Sleep - NB. this is misprinted Oct. 31st in the BBCS Devon Branch Newsletter No. 19, p. 11).

The larval foodplants are various species of fine-leaved grass.

## Pearly Heath *Coenonympha arcania* (Linnaeus)

Barrett (1893) refers to two specimens of this widely distributed European species in the collection of Major J.N. Still of Seaton. These were believed to have been caught by Still in 1866 on the coast of either Devon or Dorset. Barrett saw one of the specimens and stated that it had been correctly determined, although there was doubt as to its true provenance. W.F. Kirby (1903) stated that The Pearly Heath is said 'to have been taken in the south of England several times, especially in the south-west'. In Europe, *arcania* occurs throughout France up to the English Channel. The heath butterflies are not normally migratory, but Burton (1992) thought that the Pearly Heath was one of several European butterflies which could occasionally reach this country as a migrant. Alternatively, it may formerly have occurred on the south coast of Britain at the northern extremity of its range.

# Danaidae

## Monarch *Danaus plexippus* (Linnaeus)                      Plate 16f

This is primarily a North American species which occasionally reaches the British Isles in the autumn. The sightings are irregular, with several years passing between occurrences. The 1930s were good years for the Monarch, with thirteen being seen or captured; 1968 was also a good year with nine records, followed by the exceptional year of 1981 with nineteen occurrences. Since then, there have only been three additional records, in 1982 and 1983.

The complete Devon record in chronological order is:

1826 **Plymouth**, Sept. 8th (Stidston, 1952). If correct, it is the first record in Europe.

1885 **Exmouth**, August (Hellins, 1886:211).

1885 **Plymouth**, Sept. 25th, F.F. Freeman (Freeman, 1885); seen alive by G.F. Mathew (1921). A second specimen recorded by Stidston in Doe (1934).

1887 **Dartmouth**, September (Barrett, 1893:114) (given as 1886 in Barrett, 1906).

1917 **Instow**, Oct. 1st. Seen by G.F. Mathew (1921:211).

1925 **Wembury**, F.T. Williams (Stidston, 1952).

1926 **Countisbury**, near, Sept. 8th, S. Morris (Nicholson, 1938).

1931 **Modbury**, Oct. 3rd, H.E. Hooppell (Nicholson, 1935d); presumably the same specimen recorded by Doe (1934) from "Bigbury".

1932 **Exmouth** (Rowley, 1933).

1933 **Budleigh Salterton**, Sept. 5th, female, M. Wood (Times, Oct. 6th 1933; Frohawk, 1933). Now in the collection of Mrs M. Wood of Westbury, Wilts. (R.F. Bretherton, *pers. commn.*).

1933 **Exmouth Beach**, Oct. 1st, S.D. Gibbard (Dannreuther, 1933).

1934 **Beer [Regis]**, Aug. 2nd, Miss Mercer, 2 seen from a boat (Nicholson, 1938).

1934 **Combe Martin**, Sept. 20th, Mrs Miall (Frohawk, 1934a).

1934 **Bideford**, Sept. 27th, W.M. Littlewood (Times Oct. 3rd; Frohawk, 1934a).

1935 **South Huish**, Oct. 4th, Mr Halahan, J.O.N. Wood (Wood, 1936; Doe, 1937).

1936 **Start Point**, Aug. 11th, A.W. Godfrey (Dannreuther, 1936).

1936 **Salcombe**, Sept. 16th, Mrs Besant (Western Morning News, Sept. 22nd 1936; Dannreuther, 1936).

1937 **Slapton**, Sept. 28th, H.O. Mills (Dannreuther, 1937).

1937 **Stoke Fleming**, Sept. 28th, H.M. Churchward (Dannreuther, 1937).

1940 **Putsborough**, Nov. 4th, one female, W.R.C. Matthews, kept alive for 2 weeks; specimen in BM(NH) (Bracken, 1941).

1945 **Tiverton**, early September 1945 (Dannreuther, 1946).

1947 **Lustleigh**, Oct. 17th, J.W.G. Cavernton (Western Morning News, Jan. 6th 1948; Dannreuther, 1948).

1949 **Plymstock**, Sept. 13th, F.J. Hart (Dannreuther, 1950).

1950 **Exeter**, July 29th (Dannreuther, 1951).

1955 **Axmouth landslip**, May 5th, C.C. Champion (Wallace, 1967).

1959 **Peter Tavy**, Aug. 18th, A.M. Laird (French, 1962).

1962 **Ugborough**, October, Mr Parkhouse (Turner, 1964; French, 1964).

1962 **Ebford**, S. Toyn.

1965 **Barnstaple**, Sept. 19th. This specimen, seen, but not caught, is believed to be one of several marked specimens released at Cadbury Camp, Somerset, as part of a migration experiment (Burton, 1966).

1968 **Stokenham**, Oct. 2nd or 3rd, Mrs R. Lyon (French, 1973).

1968 **Torquay**, Oct. 3rd, W.R. Walker, and Oct. 21st, M.J. Howes (French, 1973).

1968 **Exeter**, Oct. 15th or 16th, two seen, B.Long (Dev. Ass.).

1968 **Brixham**, Oct. 16th, D. Hartley (French, 1973).

1968 **Abbotsham**, Oct. 17th, G.D. Watts (Turner, 1969).

1968 **Teignmouth**, Oct. 17th (French, 1973).

1968 **Mary Tavy**, Oct. 22nd, G.W. Markham (French, 1973).

1968 **Rousdon**, Nov. 4th, N. Yool (French, 1973).

1973 **Between Halton and Weir quays**, F.H.N. Smith (Bretherton and Chalmers-Hunt, 1982, p. 146).

1976 **Prince Hall**, near Two Bridges, 'Summer', communicated by the owner of Prince Hall to D.Smallshire in 1989.

1981 **Noss Mayo**, Sept. 25th, S. Spooner on Buddleia (Spooner, 1982).

1981 **Ilfracombe**, Tunnels Beach, Sept. 25th, K.R. Wilson (specimen in his collection) (Western Morning News, Oct. 6th, 1981).

1981 **Lundy**, Sept. 25th, C.W. Dee, and seen frequently by others during the following week (Bretherton and Chalmers-Hunt, 1982). One or two seen between Sept 25th and Oct. 2nd, R. Compey (Lundy Field Soc. & Bird Supplement, 32nd Annual Report, for 1981, p. 13.

1981 **Plymouth City Centre**, Sept. 25th or 26th (Plymouth Museum).

1981 **Plymstock**, Sept. 26th, Q. Bone (Spooner, 1982).

1981 **Kingsbridge**, Sept. 27th, V. Tucker (Bretherton and Chalmers-Hunt, 1982).

1981 **Prawle Point**, Sept. 27th, A. Archer-Lock (1981); Sept. 29th, 4, D.J.Hopkins (Bretherton and Chalmers-Hunt, 1982).

1981 **Slapton Ley**, Sept. 27th, V. Tucker and A. Archer-Lock (possibly 3 active and 1 exhausted) (Archer-Lock, 1981). See Plate 16f.

1981 **Aveton Gifford**, Sept. 26th or 27th, G.M. Spooner (Bretherton and Chalmers-Hunt, 1982).

1981 **Prawle village**, Sept. 29th, D.J. Hopkins, one at mid-day, and earlier than the Prawle Point sightings.

1981 **Slapton**, Oct. 6th (Bretherton and Chalmers-Hunt, 1982).

1981 **Newton Ferrers**, two (Bretherton and Chalmers-Hunt, 1982).

1982 **Fingles Bridge**, Aug. 10th, D. Liley (R.F. Bretherton, *pers. commn.*).

1983 **Soar Mill Cove**, Oct. 25th, R. Burridge (Bretherton and Chalmers-Hunt, 1984).

1983 **Ilfracombe**, old railway, July 27th, A. & P. Roach; July 30th, G.Lane (presumably the same specimen).

# 3. GAZETTEER

This gazetteer is intended to help those people unfamiliar with Devon to locate places mentioned in the text. The grid references correspond to the one kilometer square within which the site occurs. If the site covers several then the square given is the one with the local church included, or a range is given.

If no reference is given this is because we do not know where the original author was referring to. Multiple references mean that there are different sites known by the same name.

| | | | |
|---|---|---|---|
| Abbot's Park, Molland | [SS8027] | Berry Pomeroy | [SX8260] |
| Abbotsham | [SS4226] | Bickham Moor | [SS8621] |
| Abbotsham Cliffs | [SS4127] | Bickington | [SX7972] |
| Alphington, Exeter | [SX9189] | Bickleigh (Shaugh Bridge) | [SX5363] |
| Andrews Wood | [SS7051] | Bickleigh Vale | [SX5258-5364] |
| Appledore | [SS4530] | Bicton Common | [SY0486-0686] |
| Ashburton | [SX7569] | Bideford | [SS4426] |
| Ashclyst (Sprydon Plantation) | [SX9999] | Bindon Cliffs | [SY2689-2789] |
| Ashclyst Forest | [SY0099] | Binworthy Moor, Welsford | [SS2821-2922] |
| Ashcombe Copse, Dalwood | [ST2501] | Bishopsteignton | [SX9072] |
| Ashreigney | [SS6213] | Black Torrington | [SS4304] |
| (Ash Wood) | [SS6214] | Blackawton (Longwells Wood) | [SX8051] |
| (High Wood) | [SS6311] | Blackdown Hills | [ST1216-2215] |
| Aveton Gifford | [SX6947] | Blackpool | [SX8174] |
| Axminster | [SY2998] | Blackpool Corner | [SY3398] |
| Axmouth (Springhead) | [SY2790] | Blagdon Moor, Holsworthy | [SS3404] |
| Axmouth-Lyme Regis cliffs | [SY2689-3291] | Blanchdown Wood | [SX4273] |
| Bindon Cliffs | | Bolberry | [SX6838] |
| Charton Bay, Rousdon | | Bolt Head, Salcombe | [SX7236] |
| Dowlands Cliff | | Boreston | [SX7653] |
| Haven Cliff, Axmouth | | Bottle Hill | [SX5561] |
| Pinhay cliffs | | Bovey Down, Southleigh | [SY2091] |
| Rousdon | | Bovey Great Plantation | [SX8275] |
| Rousdon Landslip | | Bovey Heath | [SX8276] |
| Whitland Cliff landslip | | Bovey Heathfield | [SX8276] |
| Aylesbeare (Manor Plantation) | [SY0490] | Bovey Pottery works | [SX8176] |
| Aylesbeare Common | [SY0590] | Bovey Tracey | [SX8178] |
| Badgworthy Water, Malmsmead | [SS7945] | Bovey Valley Woodlands | [SX7879-7681] |
| Baggy Point, Croyde | [SS4240] | Bower Moor, Bulkworthy | [SS3915] |
| Bantham, near Kingsbridge | [SX6643] | Bradworthy Common | [SS3214-3215] |
| Barnstaple | [SS5633] | Branscombe | [SY1988] |
| Beadon Bridge, Hennock | [SX8181] | (Berry Cliff) | [SY1988] |
| Beaford Moor, Beaford | [SS5814] | (Branscombe Undercliff) | [SY1988] |
| Beaworthy | [SX4699] | (Hole) | [SY1989] |
| Beer Alston | [SX4366] | Branscombe-Beer Head | [SY1888-2288] |
| Beer Head, Beer | [SY2188] | Braunton | [SS4836] |
| Beer [Regis] | [SY2298] | Braunton Burrows | [SS4433-4537] |
| Beesands | [SX8240] | Brendon | [SS3607] |
| Beggars Bush, near Chudleigh | [SX8979] | Bridestowe | [SX5088] |
| Bere Alston | [SX4466] | Bridford | [SX8286] |
| Bere Ferrers | [SX4563] | Brixham | [SX9256] |
| Berry Head, Brixham | [SX9456] | (Sharkham Point) | [SX9354] |

138

| | | | |
|---|---|---|---|
| Furley | [ST2704] | Hele, Ilfracombe | [SS5347] |
| (Godworthy Bottom) | [ST2604] | Hemyock | [ST1313] |
| Gaddon Down, near Cullompton | [ST0711] | Hendon Moor (East Bursdon Farm) | [SS2618] |
| Gains Moor = Dunsdon Farm NNR | | Hennock | [SX8380] |
| Gallant le Bower | [SX7270] | (Reservoirs) | [SX8082] |
| Galmpton | [SX8856] | Hense Moor, Luppitt | [ST1707] |
| Galmpton Quarry | [SX8856] | Heybrook Bay | [SX4948] |
| Gara Point | [SX5246] | Highampton | [SS4804] |
| Gara Rock, Salcombe | [SX7436] | (Coombe Farm SSSI) | [SS4902] |
| Germansweek | [SX4493-4494] | Higher Hollocombe | [SS6211] |
| Goat Island | [SY2789] | Higher Metcombe | [SY0692] |
| Goodrington | [SX8858] | Hittisleigh (near) | [SX7496] |
| Great Consols Mine, Tamar Valley | [SX4273] | Hodgson Wood, Densham | [SS6412] |
| Great Plantation, Heathfield | [SX8275] | Hole | [SS4603] |
| Great Torrington | [SS4819] | Hole Farm, Highampton | [SS4703] |
| Grimspound | [SX7080] | Hollocombe | [SS6311] |
| Gunnislake (Devon side of Tamar) | [SX4270] | Hollow Moor, Highampton | [SS4700-4801] |
| Hackpen Hill, Hemyock | [ST1112] | Holne Moor | [SX6670] |
| Hakeford | [SS6135] | Holsworthy | [SS3403] |
| Haldon | [SX8784-8983] | (Simpson Farm) | [SS3604] |
| (Buller Hill) | [SX8884] | Holwill | [SS4210] |
| (Harcombe Wood) | [SX8882] | Honiton | [ST1600] |
| (Kiddens Plantation) | [SX8784] | Horrabridge | [SX5169] |
| (Tower Wood) | [SX8884] | Horrabridge Station | [SX5069] |
| Hallsands | [SX8138] | Horsey Island | [SS4733] |
| Halton and Weir quays | [SX4165-4365] | Huddisford (Marshall Farm) | [SS3118] |
| Halwill Junction | [SS4400] | Huddisford Moor, Huddisford | [SS3119] |
| Halwill Moor Plantation | [SS4200] | Huntsham | [ST0020] |
| Hannicombe Wood, Drewsteignton | [SX7489] | Huntshaw Woods, near Great Torrington | |
| Harbertonford | [SX7755] | | [SS4922] |
| Harcombe House, Haldon Moor | ?[SX8981] | Ide, Exeter | [SX8990] |
| Hardsworthy | [SS2816] | Ilfracombe | [SS5147] |
| Hares Down | [SS8320-8621] | (Warnscombe Farm) | [SS5345] |
| Bickham Moor | | Ilsington-Liverton | [SX7876-8075] |
| Knowstone Inner Moor | | Inner Froward Point, Kingswear | [SX9049] |
| Knowstone Outer Moor | | Instow | [SS4730] |
| Rackenford Moor | | Ipplepen | [SX8366] |
| Harpford Common | [SY0690] | Ivybridge | [SX6356] |
| Harpford Hill, Newton Poppleford | [SY0689] | Jennett's Reservoir (top end) | [SS4224] |
| Harpford Wood, Harpford | [SY1090] | Kenn | [SX9285] |
| Hartland | [SS2524] | Kenton | [SX9583] |
| Hartland Abbey, Hartland | [SS2424] | (Oxton House) | [SX9282] |
| Hartland Forest, Welsford | [SS2720] | King's Nympton (1km NE of) | [SS6919] |
| Hartland Point | [SS2227] | Kingford Fen, Pancrasweek | [SS2806] |
| Hartland Quay | [SS2224] | Kingsbridge | [SX7344] |
| Hatherleigh | [SS5404] | Kingskerswell | [SX8667] |
| Hatherleigh Moor | [SS5503] | Kingsteignton clay pits | [SX8674] |
| Haven Cliff, Axmouth | [SY2689] | Kingston | [SX6347] |
| Hawkchurch | [ST3400] | Kingswear | [SX8851] |
| Hawkerland Valley, Hawkerland | [SY0589] | Knowle | [SS4938] |
| Hawkswood Reserve | [SY2097] | Knowstone | [SS8223] |
| Hawkswood, Offwell | [SY2097] | Labrador Bay | [SX9370] |
| Haydon, near Kenton | [SX9383] | Ladies Mile, Dawlish | [SX9777] |
| Haytor | [SX7476] | Langtree, near Great Torrington | [SS4515] |
| Heasley Mill (Long Wood) | [SS7433-7633] | Lannacombe Cliff | [SX8037] |
| Heathfield | [SX8376] | Lapford | [SS7308] |
| Heddon's Mouth, Martinhoe | [SS6549] | Laughter Hole (near) | [SX6575] |

| | | | |
|---|---|---|---|
| Lee | [SS4846] | Newton Abbot | |
| Lee [Leigh] Moor (Dartmoor Tramway) | | (Aller Park Brake) | [SX8769] |
| | [SX5661] | (Bradley Manor) | [SX8470] |
| 'Leigh' Valley, Ilfracombe | [SS4846] | (Bradley Wood) | [SX8470] |
| Lifton | [SX3885] | (Broadridge Wood) | [SX8370-8470] |
| Lincombe Mouth | [SY1587] | (Decoy Wood) | [SX8670] |
| Littleham Cove | [SY0480] | (Decoy) | [SX8670] |
| Liverton | [SX8075] | (Jetty Marsh Lane) | [SX8671] |
| (Rora Wood) | [SX7975] | (Knowles Hill) | [SX8571] |
| Loddiswell | [SX7248] | (Milber Down) | [SX8770] |
| (Andrew's Wood) | [SX7051] | (Ogwell Mill Lane) | [SX8470] |
| Longdown | [SX8691] | (Rackerhayes) | [SX8672] |
| Lower Washfield, near Tiverton | [SS9416] | Newton Bushel = Newton Abbot | |
| Luckett Moor | [SS8324] | Newton Ferrers | [SX5448] |
| Luckroft, Northlew | [SS4700] | Newton Poppleford | [SY0889] |
| Lundy | [SS1345] | Newton St Cyres | [SX8797] |
| Lustleigh | [SX7880] | (Hundred Acre Copse) | [SX8596] |
| Lustleigh Cleave | [SX7681] | (Northridge Copse) | [SX8696] |
| Lydford | [SX5084] | North Bovey (Youldon Farm) | [SX7384] |
| (Coryhill Plantation) | [SX4783] | North Brentor | [SX4881] |
| (Lydford Station) | [SX5082] | North Tawton | [SS6601] |
| (old railway) | [SX4783-5083] | Northam | [SS4429] |
| Lympstone Common | [SY0284] | Northam Burrows | [SS4430] |
| Lynmouth | [SS7249] | Northleigh | [SY1995] |
| (Myrtleberry Cleave) | [SS7348] | Northlew | [SX5099] |
| Lynton (Lynbridge) | [SS7248] | (Scabsbury Copse) | [SS5101] |
| Maiden Down, Culmstock | [ST0816-0916] | North Wyke | [SX6698] |
| Maidencombe, Torquay | [SX9268] | Noss Mayo | [SX5447] |
| Manaton | [SX7581] | (The Warren) | [SX5346] |
| Mardon Down | [SX7687] | Nymet Bridge | [SS7109] |
| (Northmoor Bog) | [SX7587] | Nymet Wood | [SS7109] |
| Marsland RSNC Reserve | [SS2117] | Oakford | [SS8920-9021] |
| Mary Tavy | [SX5079] | (Spurway Mill) | [SS8920] |
| (Burnford Farm) | [SX4978] | (Stuckeridge) | [SS9320] |
| (Grendon Farm) | [SX4978] | Oakford Rectory | [SS9121] |
| (Hill Bridge) | [SX5380] | Okehampton | [SX5895] |
| Marystow | [SX4382] | Okehampton Castle | [SX5894] |
| Meadfoot | [SX9363] | Old Mill Reserve, Dartmouth | [SX8552] |
| Meddon (near Deptford Farm) | [SS2717] | Orley Common, Ipplepen | [SX8266] |
| Melbury Wood | [SS3619-3720] | Ottery St Mary | [SY1095] |
| Meldon Reservoir, Okehampton | [SX5590] | Padley Common, Chagford | [SX6987] |
| Membland Drive, Noss Mayo | [SX5346] | Paignton | [SX8960] |
| Membury | [ST2703] | (Clennon Hill) | [SX8859] |
| (Waterhouse Farm) | [ST2603] | (Clennon Valley) | [SX8859] |
| Mershaw Moor (Burrow Cross) | [SS7617] | (Goods yard) | [SX8860] |
| Merton (Kennick Wood) | [SS5115] | (Kings Ash) | [SX8660] |
| Modbury | [SX6551] | (Paignton Reservoir) | [SX8661] |
| Moretonhampstead | [SX7585] | (Preston Down) | [SX8862] |
| Mortehoe | [SX4545] | (Yalberton) | [SX8658] |
| Mouth Mill | [SS2926] | Pancrasweek (Wooda Farm) | [SS3009] |
| Musbury | [SY2794] | Paradise Copse, Ashclyst | [ST0101] |
| Mutters Moor, Sidmouth | [SY1087] | Parracombe | [SS6644] |
| New Bridge, Holne | [SX7170] | Perridge House, Ide, Exeter | [SX8690] |
| New Park Waste | [SX5961] | Peter Tavy | [SX5177] |
| Newcourt Wood, Sheepwash | [SS4907] | Petrockstow Moor | [SS5210] |
| Newte's Hill, Tiverton | [SS9711] | Phoenix Hayes, Stockland | [ST2503] |
| Newton Abbot | [SX8671] | Pilton | [SS5534] |

Thornbury [SS3707]
Thorndon [SX5192]
Thorne Moor [SS4014-4116]
Thornworthy [SX6784]
Throwleigh (Clannaborough Farm) [SX6691]
Thrushell River [SX5292]
Thurlestone [SX6742]
Tiverton [SS9512]
Torbryan [SX8266]
Torcross [SX8242]
Torquay [SX9164]
    (Chelston Cross) [SX9063]
    (Hope's Nose) [SX9463]
    (Ilsham Valley) [SX9363]
    (Maidencombe) [SX9268]
    (Valley of Rocks, Watcombe) [SX9267]
Torquay (Watcombe) [SX9167]
Torre [SX9064]
Torrington = Great Torrington
Totnes [SX8060]
    (Brutus Bridge) [SX8060]
    (Lake Garden) [SX8058]
    (Lake Gardens) [SX8059]
Trenchford Reservoir [SX8082]
Trusham [SX8582]
Tuckham Bridge, Bere Ferrers [SX4464]
Twitchen, Mortehoe [SS4644]
Ugborough [SX6755]
Ugbrooke [SX8778]
Under Hooken [SY2188]
Upcott Farm, near Holsworthy [SS3704]
Upcott Plantation, near Germansweek [SS4396]
Upcott, near Hatherleigh [SS5703]
Uplowman [ST0115]
Venn Down, near Thorndon Cross [SX5094]
Venn Mills (East Putford) [SS3918]
Venn Ottery Common [SY0691]
Vixen Tor [SX5474]
Walkhampton [SX5369]
Walla Brook [SX6678]
Waterhouse, Northlew [SX5198]
Watersmeet, Lynmouth [SS7448]
Welcombe [SS2218]
Wellands Copse [ST2700]
Welsford Moor [SS2720]
Wembury [SX5248]
Wembury Point [SX5048]
West Down (Walkham Valley) [SX4770]
West Down, Shaugh Prior [SX5463]
West Webburn River [SX6880-7073]
Wester New Moor [SS8225]
Westhill [SY0693]
Weston Coombe, Weston [SY1688]
Weston Mouth, Weston [SY1688]
Westward Ho! [SS4329]
    (cliffs) [SS4229]
Whiddon Down [SX6992]

Whipton [SX9493-9494]
Whiteleigh Meadow, Halwill [SS4102]
Whitestone [SX8693]
Whitland Cliff landslip [SY3090]
Widecombe (Broadaford Farm) [SX6976]
Widecombe in the Moor [SX7176]
Winkleigh [SS6308]
Wiston Moor [SS8224]
Witheridge Moor [SS8515-8616]
Withleigh, Buzzards [SS9011]
Wolf River, E. Grinnacombe-Hennard Jefford,
=Roadford [SX4292]
Wonford, Exeter [SX9491]
Wonham, near Oakford [SS9221]
Woodbury [SY0087]
Woodbury Castle [SY0286]
Woodbury Common [SY0387]
Woodford Bridge, Westward Ho! [SS4228]
Woolacombe [SS4543]
Woolfardisworthy [SS3321]
    (Higher West Town Farm) [SS3221]
    (Kennerland Farm) [SS3322]
Woolston Green, Staverton [SX7766]
Wotter, Shaugh Prior [SX5561]
Wrangaton [SX6757]
Yarcombe [ST2408]
Yard Moor, Ponsworthy [SX6974]
Yarner Wood [SX7778-7878]
Yealm district = ?Yealmpton
Yealmpton [SX5751]
Yelland [SS4931]
Yelverton [SX5267]
Yeoford [SX7898]
Youlston Wood, near Barnstaple [SS6035-6036]

# 4. REFERENCES

Aldridge, R. 1946. *Caradrina superstes* in Devon. *Entomologist*, **79**: 208.

Allan, P.B.M. 1980. *Leaves from a moth-hunter's notebooks*. Farringdon: Classey.

Anonymous. 1894. [Small collection of Lepidoptera made in Lundy Isle by Mr R.W. Chase.]. *Entomologist*, **27**: 203.

Anonymous. 1927. Noteworthy Entomological Records for the Season 1925-6. *Trans. & Proc. Torquay Nat. Hist. Soc.*, **4**: 381-382.

Anonymous. 1931. Noteworthy Entomological Records and Observations for the Season 1929-30. *Trans. & Proc. Torquay Nat. Hist. Soc.*, **5**: 365-366.

Anonymous. 1946. Entomological notes. *Trans. & Proc. Torquay Nat. Hist. Soc.*, **9**: 152.

Anonymous. 1962. Zoology (including Entomology). *J. Torquay Nat. Hist. Soc.*, **13**(3): 34-36.

Anonymous. 1988. Help save Hisley Wood. *The Woodland Trust News*, No. 27: 4.

Archer-Lock, A. 1979. Bagpipes and Cider. *Ent. Rec. & J. Var.*, **91**: 211-212.

Archer-Lock, A. 1980a. Behaviour of Painted Lady (*Cynthia cardui*). *Ent. Rec. & J. Var.*, **92**: 87.

Archer-Lock, A. 1980b. The White-letter Hairstreak: *Strymondia w-album* Knoch. *Ent. Rec. & J. Var.*, **92**: 254-255.

Archer-Lock, A. 1980c. Late appearances, 1980. *Ent. Rec. & J. Var.*, **92**: 266.

Archer-Lock, A. 1981. The Monarch: *Danaus plexippus* L. in England, 1981. *Ent. Rec. & J. Var.*, **93**: 199-201.

Asher, J. 1989. Holly Blue. *Butterfly News (BBCS)*, No. 43: 10.

Barrett, C.G. 1893. *The Lepidoptera of the British Isles*. Vol. 1. London: L. Reeve & Co.

Barrett, C.G. 1906. Lepidoptera. Victoria County History. *Devon*. **1**: 208-230.

Basden-Smith, H.W. 1894. Plymouth. *Ent. Rec. & J. Var.*, **5**: 16-17.

[Bastow, K.], 1990. Green Chequered White (*Pieris daplidice*) in Newton Abbot. *British Butt. Cons. Soc. (Devon Branch) Newsletter*, No. 14: 10-11.

Battersby, W.H. 1859. Occurrence of *Vanessa Antiopa* at Torquay. *Zoologist*, **17**: 6461-6462.

Bedford, C.E. 1897. *Callimorpha hera* etc. at Dawlish. *Entomologist*, **30**: 123.

Bell, J.H. [1933]. *Days with a butterfly net*. London: Watkin & Doncaster.

Bignell, G.C. 1865. *Lycaena Arion* near Plymouth. *Entomologist*, **2**: 295.

Bignell, G.C. 1884a. Entomological Notes, Captures, &c. *Lycaena Arion*. *Entomologist*, **17**: 208-9.

Bignell, G.C. 1884b. Notes on *Lycaena Arion*. *Entomologist's Monthly Magazine*, **21**: 87.

Blathwayt, C.S.H. 1945. Immigration of *Pontia daplidice*. *Entomologist*, **78**: 124-125.

Blathwayt, F.L. 1909. *Lycaena corydon* in Devonshire. *Entomologist*, **42**: 211-212; 323.

Bostock, G.J. 1857. Captures near Bideford. *Entomologist's Weekly Intelligencer*, **2**: 108-109.

Bowles, N. 1990. The butterflies of 1990. *Butterfly News (BBCS)*, No. 46: 18-22.

Bracken, C.W. 1934. *Polygonia c-album* near Plymouth. *Entomologist*, **67**: 39.

Bracken, C.W. 1935. Comma Butterfly. Scarcity of Records in West This Year. *Western Morning News* (between Aug. 1st and 14th).

Bracken, C.W. 1936. Westward Drift of the Comma Butterfly. *Rep. & Trans. Devonshire Ass.*, **68**: 135-137.

Bracken, C.W. 1940a. Devon Entomologists and Entomology. *Rep. & Trans. Devonshire Ass.*, **72**: 23-61.

Bracken, C.W. 1940b. Entomology. In Forty-fifth Report on Scientific Memoranda. *Rep. & Trans. Devonshire Ass.*, **72**: 128-130.

Bracken, C.W. 1943. Forty-eighth Report of Scientific Memoranda. *Rep. & Trans. Devonshire Ass.*, **75**: 83-87.

Bracken, C.W. 1944. Forty-ninth Report of Scientific Memoranda. *Rep. & Trans. Devonshire Ass.*, **76**: 83-85.

Bracken, C.W. 1945. Fiftieth Report of Scientific Memoranda. *Rep. & Trans. Devonshire Ass.*, **77**: 99-101.

Bracken, C.W. 1946. Fifty-first Report of Scientific Memoranda. *Rep. & Trans. Devonshire Ass.*, **78**: 85-87.

Bracken, C.W. 1947. Fifty-second Report of Scientific Memoranda. *Rep. & Trans. Devonshire Ass.*, **79**: 51-53.

Bracken, C.W. 1948. Fifty-third Report of Scientific Memoranda. *Rep. & Trans. Devonshire Ass.*, **80**: 73-76.

Bretherton, R.F. 1983. Lepidoptera Immigration to the British Isles, 1969 to 1977. *Proc. & Trans. Br. Ent. & Nat. Hist. Soc.*, **161**: 1-23.

Bretherton, R.F. and Chalmers-Hunt, J.M. 1982. The immigration of lepidoptera to the British Isles in 1981, including that of the Monarch butterfly: *Danaus plexippus* L. Annexe III. *Ent. Rec. & J. Var.*, **94**: 141-146.

Bretherton, R.F. and Chalmers-Hunt, J.M. 1984. The immigration of lepidoptera to the British Isles in 1983. Annex II. *Ent. Rec. & J. Var.*, **96**: 149-159.

Bretherton, R.F. and Chalmers-Hunt, J.M. 1990. The immigration of lepidoptera into the British Isles in 1989. *Ent. Rec. & J. of Var.*, **102**: 153-159; 215-224.

Bristow, C.R. 1987. The Wall Butterfly. *British Butt. Cons. Soc. (Devon Branch) Newsletter*, No. 3: 5.

Bristow, C.R. and Bolton, D.E. 1986. *Devon Butterflies. Provisional Atlas 1986.* Exeter: Royal Albert Memorial Museum.

Bristow, C.R. and Bolton, D.E. 1988. *Devon Butterflies. Provisional Atlas 1988.* Exeter: Royal Albert Memorial Museum.

Bristowe, W.S. 1967. The life of a distinguished woman naturalist, Eleanor Glanville (*circa* 1654-1709). *Entomologist's Gazette*, **18**: 202-211.

Brooking Rowe, J. 1870. Natural history notes. *J. Plymouth Inst.*, **4**: 154-156.

Brown, J. 1876. *Lycaena arion. Entomologist*, **9**: 204.

Browne, G.B. 1904. A Fortnight's Collecting at Dawlish. *Proc. S. Lond. Ent. & Nat. Hist. Soc.*, 1903, pp. 22-28.

Bruce, L. 1987. Summer's Hesitant Start. *Mid-Devon Advertiser*, Friday July 24th.

Buckland, J. 1894. *Vanessa polychloros* in Devon. *Entomologist*, **27**: 272.

Burton, J. 1966. Report on Monarch butterfly (*Danaus plexippus*) Migration experiment, 1965. *Entomologist's Monthly Magazine*, **102**: 3-4.

Burton, J.F. 1992. Why was 1887 an exceptional year for vagrant butterflies in Britain. *Ent. Rec. & J. Var.*, **104**: 25-31.

Burton, R.J. 1944. "Commencing a collection in North Devon". *Proc. & Trans. S. Lond. Ent. & Nat. Hist. Soc.* 1943-44: 28-39.

Carr, F.M.B. 1955. Notes on Collecting in 1955. *Ent. Rec. & J. Var.*, **67**: 258-260; 307-309.

Carrington, J.T. 1887. Reported occurrence of *Polyommatus gordius* in Devonshire. *Entomologist*, **20**: 173.

Catt, M. 1992. South Devon migrants '91. *Butterfly Conservation News*, No. 51, 26.

Chalmers-Hunt, J.M. 1977. The 1976 Invasion of the Camberwell Beauty (*Nymphalis antiopa* L.). *Ent. Rec. & J. Var.*, **89**: 89-105.

Chalmers-Hunt, J.M. 1983. Obituary. T.D.Fearnehough. *Ent. Rec. & J. Var.*, **95**: 114.

Chanter, J.R. 1877. *Lundy Island, a Monograph, Descriptive and Historical.* Cassell, Petter & Galpin.

Cole, A.K. 1986. Letter in *Butterfly News (BBCS)*, No. 36: 22.

Coleridge, W.L. 1973. The scarce painted lady in Devon. *Bull. Am. Ent. Soc.*, **32**: 33.

Coxhead, J.R.W. 1970. Butterflies in south-east Devon. *Quart. J. Devon Trust for Nat. Cons.*, **2**: 125-128.

Cribb, P.W. 1960. Further Observations on the Butterflies of Southern France and the French Alps, 1960. *Bull. Am. Ent. Soc.*, **19**: 115-117.

Croft, E.O. 1929. *Polygonia c-album* in Devon. *Entomologist*, **52**: 201.

Crotch, W.D. 1857. Doings in the West. *Entomologist's Weekly Intelligencer*, **2**: 165-166.

Dannreuther, T. 1933. Migration Records. *Entomologist*, **66**: 251-257.

Dannreuther, T. 1936. Migration Records. *Entomologist*, **69**: 255-259.

Dannreuther, T. 1937. Migration records, 1937. *Entomologist*, **70**: 250-254.

Dannreuther, T. 1943. Migration records, 1942. *Entomologist*, **76**: 73-80.

Dannreuther, T. 1946. Records of the Bath White (*Pontia daplidice* (L.)) observed in the British Isles during 1945. *J. Soc. Br. Ent.*, **3**: 1-7.

Dannreuther, T. 1946. Migration Records, 1945. *Entomologist*, **79**: 97-110.

Dannreuther, T. 1948. Migration Records, 1947. *Entomologist*, **81**: 73-83; 110-117.

Dannreuther, T. 1949. Corrections and additions to the 1945 records of the Bath White (*Pontia daplidice* (L.)) and the Long-tailed Blue (*Lampides boeticus* (L.)) (Lep.). *J. Soc. Br. Ent.*, **3**: 48-49.

Dannreuther, T. 1950. Migration Records, 1949. *Entomologist*, **83**: 129-133.

Dannreuther, T. 1951. Migration Records, 1950. *Entomologist*, **84**: 85-90; 102-106.

Dele, J.S. 1858. *Vanessa antiopa. Entomologist's Monthly Magazine*, **4**: 179.

Dell, J.S. 1858. An Entomological Excursion to Shaugh Common and Bickleigh Vale. *Entomologist's Weekly Intelligencer*, **4**: 82-83.

Demuth, R.P. 1985. Reminiscences of an elderly entomologist. *Ent. Rec. & J. Var.*, **97**: 13-19.

Dobson, A.H. 1969. Devon Lepidoptera. *J. Devon Trust Nat. Cons.*, No. 21: 908-915.

Doe, G.M. 1930. Thirty-Seventh Report of Scientific Memoranda. *Rep. & Trans. Devonshire Ass.*, **62**: 187-194.

Doe, G.M. 1934. Fortieth Report of Scientific Memoranda. *Rep. & Trans. Devonshire Ass.*, **66**: 121-128.

Doe, G.M. 1935. Forty-first Report on Scientific Memoranda. *Rep. & Trans. Devonshire Ass.*, **67**: 208.

Doe, G.M. 1937. Forty-third Report on Scientific Memoranda. *Rep. & Trans. Devonshire Ass.*, **69**: 199-207.

Doe, G.M. 1938. Forty-fourth Report on Scientific Memoranda. *Rep. & Trans. Devonshire Ass.*, **70**: 117-125.

Doe, G.M. 1941. Forty-sixth Report on Scientific Memoranda. *Rep. & Trans. Devonshire Ass.*, **73**: 105-108.

Doe, G.M. 1942. Forty-seventh Report of Scientific Memoranda. *Rep. & Trans. Devonshire Ass.*, **74**: 105-107.

Dowdeswell, W.H. 1981. *The Life of the Meadow Brown.* London: Heinemann Ltd.

D'Urban, W.S.M. 1865. Exeter Naturalists' Club. *Entomologist's Monthly Magazine*, **2**: 71.

Dymond, J.N. 1973. Butterflies in 1972. *Lundy Field Soc., 23rd Ann. Rep. 1972*: 38.

Dymond, J.N. 1974. Butterflies and moths. *Lundy Field Soc., 24th Ann. Rep. 1973*: 24-27.

Elliot, E.A.S. 1915. Some points of interest on the Natural History of the Plateau known as the Sores or Sae Wares (A.-S. Dwellers by the Sea). *Rep. & Trans. Devonshire Ass.*, **47**: 396-406.

Emmet, A.M. and Heath, J. 1989. *The Moths and Butterflies of Great Britain and Ireland,* Vol. 7(1). Colchester: Harley Books.

Ford, E.B. 1945a. *Argynnis euphrosyne* in mid-April, 1945. *Entomologist*, **78**: 79.

Ford, E.B. 1945b. *Butterflies.* London: Collins.

Fox, S.P. 1874. *Kingsbridge and Its Surroundings.* Kingsbridge: S.P.Fox. pp. 260-261, Appendix D, Butterflies by H.Nicholls.

Freeman, F.F. 1885. Exhibitions etc. *Proc. Ent. Soc. Lond.*, in *Trans. Ent. Soc. Lond.*, **18** (for 1886), p. xxv.

French, R.A. 1953. Insect migration Records, 1952. *Entomologist*, **86**: 157-164.

French, R.A. 1957. Migration records 1956. *Entomologist*, **90**: 227-238.

French, R.A. 1958. Migration Records 1957. *Entomologist*, **91**: 101-109.

French, R.A. 1962. Migration Records 1961. *Entomologist*, **95**: 169-177.

French, R.A. 1963. Rarer Vagrant Insects Recorded in the British Isles in 1961. *Entomologist*, **96**: 36-38.

French, R.A. 1964. Migration Records 1962. *Entomologist*, **97**: 121-128.

French, R.A. 1971. Migration Records, 1966 and 1967. *Entomologist*, **104**: 204-218.

French, R.A. 1973. Migration Records, 1968. *Entomologist*, **106**: 256-263.

Frohawk, F.W. 1896. Early appearances of *Lycaena argiolus, Pararge aegeria* and *Smerinthus ocellatus. Entomologist*, **29**: 165.

Frowhawk, F.W. 1934a. In Devon. *Entomologist*, **67**: 248.

Frowhawk, F.W. 1934b. *The complete book of British Butterflies.* London: Ward, Lock & Co.

Frost, M.P. and Madge, S.C. 1991. *Butterflies in south-east Cornwall.* Caradon Field and Nat. Hist. Club.

Gainsford, P. 1971. Exhibits - annual exhibition. *Proc. & Trans. Br. Ent. & Nat. Hist. Soc.,* 4: 11.

Gainsford, P. 1974. *Mellicta athalia* Rott. in East Cornwall, 1974. *Ent. Rec. & J. Var.,* 87: 172-175.

Garrett-Jones, C. 1969. Early-July on Lundy: Butterflies and moths recorded. *Lundy Field Soc., Nineteenth Ann. Rep.,* pp. 30-33.

Gatcombe, J. 1869. *Lycaena Arion,* &c., in Devon: *Melitaea Cinxia* in Dorset, &c. *Entomologist,* 4: 301.

Gibbes, H. 1858. Duplicate Lepidoptera. *Entomologist's Weekly Intelligencer,* 4: 127.

Glover, S. 1987. The clifftop haunt of the Adonis Blue. *British Butt. Cons. Soc. (Devon Branch) Newsletter,* No. 2: 3.

Goater, B. 1971. Probable American painted lady (*Vanessa virginiensis* (Drury)) (Lep., Nymphalidae) in North Devon. *Entomologist's Gazette,* 22: 54.

Goss, H. 1877. Further notes on *Lycaena arion. Entomologist,* 10: 96-97.

Greenwood, J.J.D. 1963. Butterflies. *Lundy Field Soc.15th Ann. Rep.,* p. 21.

Harding, R.C. 1986. *Butterflies and larger insects of the Braunton area.* Braunton Conservation Project.

Harvey, L.A. and St. Leger-Gordon, D. 1953. *Dartmoor.* London: Collins.

Harvie, R.P. 1866. Captures in South Devon. *Entomologist's Weekly Intelligencer,* 9: 51-52.

Heath, J. 1946. *The Lepidoptera,* 159pp. Typescript, privately circulated.

Heckford, R.J. 1984. Notes on *Tebenna bjerkandrella* (Thunberg). *Ent. Rec. & J. Var.,* 96: 58-63.

Hellins, J. 1886. *Danais Archippus* at Exmouth. *Entomologist's Monthly Magazine,* 22: 211.

Henderson, J. 1885. Notes on Lundy Island. *Young Naturalist,* 6: 216.

Henderson, J. 1886. Another visit to Lundy. *Young Naturalist,* 8: 181-183.

Henstock, H. 1934. Short Notes of Nature Observations. *Proc. College Field Club & Nat. Hist. Soc.,* 1932-33: 12-13.

Henwood, B.P. 1990. Larvae of the Brown Argus, *Aricia agestis* D&S (Lep.: Lycaenidae) feeding on the seeds of *Geranium molle. Ent. Rec. & J. Var.,* 102: 45.

Heslop, I.R.P. 1958. An occurrence of *Papilio podalirius* in Devon. *Entomologist's Gazette,* 9: 44.

Hinchcliff, K.M. 1893. North Devon. *Ent. Rec. & J. Var.,* 4: 180-181.

Holroyd, G.C. 1952. *Argynnis lathonia* in Devon. *Entomologist,* 85: 244.

Howarth, T.J. 1973. *South's British butterflies.* London: Warne & Co.

Huggins, H. 1983. Start Point, 21st Sept. 1980. *Devon Birds,* 36: 63-65.

Hunt, O.D. 1964. The 'Large Blue' Butterfly. *J. Devon Trust Nat. Cons.,* No. 2: 77-79.

Hunt, O.D. 1965. *Status and conservation of the large blue butterfly, Maculinea arion* L.: pp. 35-44. In Duffey, E. and Morris, M.G. (Eds.), *The conservation of invertebrates.* Monks Wood Experimental Station Symposium No. 1.

Hunt, R. 1960. News from Members. *Bull. Am. Ent. Soc.,* 19: 14.

Hyde, G.E. 1983. The Queen of Spain Fritillary reared from eggs. *Ent. Rec. & J. Var.,* 95: 180.

Ivimey-Cook, R.B. 1984. *Atlas of the Devon Flora.* Exeter: Devonshire Association.

Jeffery, F.W. 1942. Records of Devon Lepidoptera. *Entomologist,* 75: 261.

Jeffery, F.W. 1943. *Pyrameis huntera* in England. *Entomologist,* 76: 106.

Jenkyn, T. 1968. Notes on butterflies in a coniferous forest. *J. Devon Trust Nat. Cons.,* No. 19: 818.

Jermyn, L. 1827. *The butterfly collector's Vade Mecum.* (Second edn.). Ipswich and London.

Jones, M. 1986. The large blue is back where it belongs. *Nature,* 324: 28.

Jordan, R.C.R. 1843. Note on the occurrence of *Polyommati* in South Devon. *Zoologist,* 2: 398.

Jordan, W.R.H. 1842. List of lepidoptera captured in the vicinity of Teignmouth. *Entomologist,* 1: 389-391.

Jordan, W.R.H. 1874. Notes on the Natural History of Teignmouth and its vicinity. *Rep. & Trans. Devonshire Ass.*, **6**: 712-714.

Joy, N.H. 1931. The Large Blue (*Lycaena arion*) and the Queen-of-Spain Fritillary (*Argynnis lathonia*) in North Devon. *Entomologist's Monthly Magazine*, **67**: 182.

Kerr, W.J. 1926. *Lampides Boeticus* in South Devon. *Entomologist*, **59**: 312.

Kettlewell, H.B.D. 1946. Further observations on the season 1945, with special reference to *Pontia daplidice*, etc. *Entomologist*, **79**: 111-115.

Kipping, S. 1894. Notes from Holsworthy, N. Devon. *Entomologist*, **27**: 297.

Kirby, W.D. 1903. III. Entomology. *Rep. & Trans. Devonshire Ass.*, **35**: 131.

Kirby, W.F. 1903. *The Butterflies and Moths of Europe*. London: Cassell & Co. Ltd.

Lethbridge, E. 1857. Lepidoptera at Plymouth. *Entomologist's Weekly Intelligencer*, **12**: 116.

Levett, R.J.R. 1951. Butterflies in South Devon. *Ent. Rec & J. Var.*, **63**: 182-183.

Lighton, T. 1843. Note on the occurrence of *Mancipium Daplidice* and *Argynnis Lathonia* near Exeter. *Zoologist*, **2**: 398.

Locke, M. 1950. Distribution Range of *Thymelicus lineola*. *Entomologist*, **83**: 19.

Longstaff, G.B. 1867. Capture of *Sterrha sacraria* and other Lepidoptera in Devon &c. *Entomologist's Monthly Magazine*, **4**: 131-132.

Longstaff, G.B. 1900. Some common Lepidoptera in North Devon. *Entomologist's Monthly Magazine*, **36**: 42.

Longstaff, G.B. 1902. Lepidoptera observed in the Parish of Mortehoe, North Devon. *Entomologist's Monthly Magazine*, **38**: 19-29.

Longstaff, G.B. 1903; 1904. Further notes on Lepidoptera observed at Mortehoe, North Devon. *Entomologist's Monthly Magazine*, **39**: 194-197; **40**: 29-32.

Longstaff, G.B. 1907a. First notes on the Lepidoptera of Lundy Island. *Entomologist's Monthly Magazine*, **44**: 241 (reprinted in Longstaff, 1907b).

Longstaff, G.B. 1907b. *Lepidoptera and Other Insects Observed in the Parish of Mortehoe, N. Devon*. (3rd edn.). London: Mitchell, Hughes & Clarke.

Loyd, L.R.W. 1925. *Lundy, its History and Natural History*. London: Longman, Green & Co.

Luckens, C.J. 1980. The Heath Fritillary, *Mellicta athalia* Rott. in Britain; Notes on Distribution and Ecology. *Ent. Rec. & J. Var.*, **92**: 229-234.

Lupton, H. 1911. Fauna and flora of Torquay district. *J. Torquay Nat. Hist. Soc.*, **1**: 127-134.

Majendie, R.S. 1891. Lepidoptera of Sidmouth. *Ent. Rec. & J. Var.*, **2**: 114-116.

Mallock, M. 1865. Supposed New British Butterfly. *Entomologist*, **2**: 312.

Manley, G.E.L. 1955. Immigrants noted during 1955. *Ent. Rec. & J. Var.*, **67**: 330.

Mathews, M.A. 1857. Doings in the West. *Entomologist's Weekly Intelligencer*, **2**: 189-190.

Mathew, G.F. 1858a. A Day in the Woods last March. *Entomologist's Weekly Intelligencer*, **3**: 115.

Mathew, G.F. 1858b. Captures near Barnstaple. *Entomologist's Weekly Intelligencer*, **4**: 92.

Mathew, G.F. 1858c. List of Insects taken at Barnstaple etc. 1858. *Entomologist's Weekly Intelligencer*, **5**: 68-70.

Mathew, G.F. 1860. Insects taken in the neighbourhood of Barnstaple. *Entomologist's Weekly Intelligencer*, **7**: 121.

Mathew, G.F. 1868. *Grapta C-album* in Devonshire. *Entomologist's Monthly Magazine*, **5**: 147.

Mathew, G.F. 1877. Notes on *Lycaena arion*. *Entomologist*, **10**: 35-40; 70-73.

Mathew, G.F. 1878. Rare Lepidoptera near Dartmouth. *Entomologist's Monthly Magazine*, **14**: 157.

Mathew, G.F. 1916. Notes and Observations. *Entomologist*, **49**: 287-288.

Mathew, G.F. 1921. Notes on the occurrence of *Anosia plexippus* in England. *Entomologist*, **54**: 210-211.

Mayor, C.M. 1919a. Twenty-five years in S. Devon. A Lepidopterist retrospect. *Entomologist's Monthly Magazine*, **35**: 28-32; 79-83.

Mayor, C.M. 1919b. *Eugonia polychloros* in Devon. *Entomologist*, **52**: 261.

Merrin, J. 1899. The 'extinct' *Chrysophanus dispar*. *Ent. Rec. & J. Var.*, **11**: 208-209.

Milman, P.P. 1942. *Lampides boeticus*. *Entomologist*, **75**: 68

Millman, P.P. 1943. *Limenites camilla* in Mid-Devon. *Entomologist*, 76: 145.

Morley, C. 1910. George Carter Bignell. *Entomologist*, 43: 128.

Morris, F.O. 1876. *A History of British Butterflies*. London: G. Bell & Sons.

Murdoch, R. 1988. Does the Brimstone have an alternative foodplant? *British Butt. Cons. Soc. (Devon Branch) Newsletter*, No. 6: 8.

Newman, E. 1869. *The illustrated natural history of British Butterflies*. London: D. Bogue.

Nicholls, H. 1875. *Lycaena Arion* near Kingsbridge. *Entomologist*, 8: 222.

Nicholson, C. 1933. *Apatura iris* visiting Great Knapweed. *Entomologist*, 66: 111.

Nicholson, C. 1935a. Comma butterfly. August Observation In 1933 At Launceston. *Western Morning News*, March 3rd 1935.

Nicholson, C. 1935b. Comma Butterflies. Still Scarce in Cornwall. *Western Morning News*, Aug. 14th 1935.

Nicholson, C. 1935c. Comma in Cornwall. *Western Morning News*, Nov. 6th 1935.

Nicholson, C. 1935d. *Danaus plexippus* L. in the British Isles. *Entomologist*, 68: 245-251; 269-273.

Nicholson, C. 1938. Further Notes on *Danaus plexippus* L. in the British Isles. *Entomologist*, 71: 217-225.

Norcombe, E.S. 1857. *Pamphila acteon. Entomologist's Weekly Intelligencer*, 2: 28.

Palmer, M.G. (Ed.). 1946. *The fauna and flora of the Ilfracombe district of North Devon*, xii, 266pp, 8pls, 1 map. Exeter: J. Townsend & Co.

Parfitt, E. 1856. *Melitea Athalia* and *Artemis. Entomologist's Weekly Intelligencer*, 1: 117.

Parfitt, E. 1878. Fauna of Devon. Lepidoptera. *Rep. & Trans. Devonshire Ass.*, 10: 411-588.

Parfitt, E. 1884. *Thais Polyxena* captured in England. *Entomologist's Monthly Magazine*, 21: 34.

Parkinson Curtis, W. 1929. *Lycaena arion. Entomolosist*, 52: 248.

Perkins, R.C.L. 1936. Twenty-five Years of Insect-Collecting in Devon. *J. Torquay Nat. Hist. Soc.*, 7(II): 19-26.

Perkins, R.C.L. 1945a. *Lampides boeticus* L. and other immigrant Lepidoptera in Devon. *Entomologist's Monthly Magazine*, 81: 216.

Perkins, R.C.L. 1945b. *Pontia daplidice*, (Lepidoptera: Pieridae) in Devon and Cornwall. *Entomologist's Monthly Magazine*, 81: 216.

Perkins, R.C.L. 1946. Autumnal butterflies in Devon. *Entomologist's Monthly Magazine*, 82: 43.

Petiver, J. 1702-1706. *Gazophylacii naturae & artis: decas prima - decas decima*. London.

Petiver, J. 1717. *Papilionum Britanniae icones*, 2pp, 6pls. London.

Phillips, W.J.L. 1901. *Vanessa antiopa* in Devonshire. *Entomologist*, 34: 316.

Pollard, E., Hooper, M.D. and Moore, N.W. 1974. *Hedges*. London: Collins.

Polwhele, R. 1797. *The History of Devonshire*, Vol. 1. London: Cadell, Johnson and Dilly.

Porritt, G.T. 1901. *Leucania vitellina, L. albipuncta, Laphygma exigua, Heliothis armigera* etc. in South Devon. *Entomologist's Monthly Magazine*, 37: 11-12.

Pratt, C.R. 1986-87. A history and investigation into the fluctuations of *Polygonia c-album* L.: the comma butterfly. *Ent. Rec. & J. Var.*, Vol. 98: 197-203; 244-250; 99: 21-27; 69-80.

Prideaux, R.M. 1892. *Lycaena Arion* in South Devon. *Entomologist*, 25: 221.

Prideaux, R.M. 1896. Stray Notes on the *Diurni* during 1895. *Entomologist*, 29: 89-92.

Prideaux, R.M. 1929. *Thecla w-album* in the West of England. *Entomologist*, 52: 256.

Randall Parkes, W. 1929. *Thecla w-album* in North Devon. *Entomologist*, 52: 223.

Rawlinson, W.G. 1858. Captures near Dawlish, Devon. *Entomologist's Weekly Intelligencer*, 4: 156.

Read, M. 1986. Heathland and the Silver-studded Blue in Devon. *Nature in Devon*, No. 7: 5-18.

Reading, J.J. 1862. A Catalogue of the Lepidoptera of Devon and Cornwall. Part 1. *Ann. Rep. & Trans. Plymouth Inst. & Devon and Cornwall Nat. Hist. Soc.*, 1861-62, 1, 43-64.

Richardson, A. 1947. In The Annual Exhibition - Record of Exhibits. *Proc. & Trans. S. Lond. Ent. & Nat. Hist. Soc.*, 1946-47: 40-41.

Riding, W.S. 1883. A Month at Mortehoe, North Devon. *Entomologist*, 16: 246-249.

Riley, J.A. 1947. [Untitled]. *Proc. & Trans. S. Lond. Ent. & Nat. Hist. Soc.*, 1946-47: 20.

Rogers, E.A. 1903. Notes on collecting Lepidoptera in South Devon in 1902. *Ent. Rec. & J. Var.*, **15**: 18-21.

Rowley, F.R. 1933. Short Notes and records by Members. *Proc. College Field Club & Nat. Hist. Soc.*, 1931-32: 4.

Russwurm, A.D.A. 1978. *Aberrations of British Butterflies*. Faringdon: E.W. Classey Ltd.

St. Leger-Gordon, R.E. 1934. Letter to *Western Morning News*, Oct. 19th 1934.

Scott, J.G.M. 1947. *Argynnis lathonia* in Devon. *Entomologist*, **80**: 268.

Sheldon, W.G. 1925. The destruction of British Butterflies. *Entomologist*, **58**: 105-112

Sheldon, W.G. 1929. *Lycaena arion* in south Devon; an inquiry as to its present existence. *Entomologist*, **52**: 25-26.

Sherlock, R.J. 1943. *Papilio machaon* in Devon. *Entomologist*, **76**: 207.

Sherwood, B.R. 1975. Outline survey of the rhopalocera of Lundy. *Lundy Field Society 25th Ann. Rep. 1974*: 70; 72-73.

Sitters, H.P. 1988. *Tetrad Atlas of the Breeding Birds of Devon*. Yelverton: Devon Bird Watching and Preservation Society.

Skinner, B.F. 1974. Communications. *Proc. & Trans. Br. Ent. & Nat. Hist. Soc.*, **7**: 62.

Sleep, T.D. 1989. Lydford Habitat. *British Butt. Cons. Soc. (Devon Branch) Newsletter*, No. 12: 10-11.

Smith, A.Z. 1986. *A history of the Hope Entomological Collections in the University Museum, Oxford*. Oxford: Clarendon Press.

Smith, F. 1865. Notes on *Cynthia cardui* and *Vanessa antiopa*. *Entomologist's Monthly Magazine*, **2**: 161.

Solly, R.V. [1932], Butterflies and Moths of the Neighbourhood of Exeter. *Proc. College Field Club & Nat. Hist. Soc.*, 1930-31: 9-15.

South, R. 1906. *The Butterflies of the British Isles*. London: F. Warne & Co.

Speed, A.W. 1977. Observations on Butterflies at Hilton, Derbyshire, 1970-76, and a day in Devon. *Ent. Rec. & J. Var.*, **89**: 205-208.

Spooner, G.M. 1963. On Causes of the Decline of *Maculinea arion* L. (Lepidoptera: Lycaenidae) in Britain. *Entomologist*, **96**: 199-210.

Spooner, G.M. 1982. Note on the occurrence of Monarch (or Milkweed) butterfly (*Danaus plexippus* L.). *Rep. & Trans. Devonshire Ass.*, **114**: 186-187.

Stainton, H.T. 1857. *A manual of British butterflies and moths*. Vol. 1, xii, 338pp. London.

Stidston, S.T. 1950. Second Report of the Entomological Section. *Rep. & Trans. Devonshire Ass.*, **82**: 137-157.

Stidston, S.T. 1951. Third Annual Report of the Entomological Section. *Rep. & Trans. Devonshire Ass.*, **83**: 90-101.

Stidston, S.T. 1952. *A list of the Lepidoptera of Devon*. Part 1: and Introduction. Exeter: Devonshire Association.

Stidston, S.T. 1952a. Fourth Annual Report of the Entomological Section. *Rep. & Trans. Devonshire Ass.*, **84**: 314-323.

Stidston, S.T. 1953. Fifth Annual Report of the Entomological Section. *Rep. & Trans. Devonshire Ass.*, **85**: 236-241.

Stidston, S.T. 1954. 6th Annual Report of the Entomological Section. *Rep. & Trans. Devonshire Ass.*, **86**: 309-318.

Stidston, S.T. 1955. 7th Annual Report of the Entomological Section. *Rep. & Trans. Devonshire Ass.*, **87**: 367-372.

Stidston, S.T. 1956. 8th Annual report of the Entomological Section. *Rep. & Trans. Devonshire Ass.*, **88**: 270-280.

Stidston, S.T. 1958. 10th Annual report of the Entomological Section. *Rep. & Trans. Devonshire Ass.*, **90**: 200-209.

Stidston, S.T. 1959. 11th Annual Report of the Entomological Section. *Rep. & Trans. Devonshire Ass.*, **91**: 154-164.

Stidston, S.T. 1961. 13th Annual Report of the Entomological Section. *Rep. & Trans. Devonshire Ass.*, **93**: 36-43.

Still, J.N. 1894. Occurrences of Second Broods of Lepidoptera in Devon during 1893. *Entomologist*, **27**: 18.

Stokes, H.G. 1947. *Maculinea arion* L. (Lep. Lycaenidae) in North Devon. *Entomologist's Monthly Magazine*, **83**: 247.

Stroyan, H.L.G. 1942. Devonshire Records, 1942. *Entomologist*, **75**: 261.

Tait, R. 1915. Lepidoptera taken at Branscombe, S. Devon, June 1914. *Entomologist*, **48**: 71.

"Talpa" [=J.Hellins], 1859. List of Captures in the Neighbourhood of Exeter (or rather in the lower part of the Valley of the Exe) during 1857 and 1858. *Entomologist's Weekly Intelligencer*, **5**: 131-133.

Thomas, J.A. 1977. The ecology of the large blue butterfly. *Ann. Rep. Inst. Terrestrial Ecology 1976*: 25-27.

Thomas, J.A. 1980. Why Did the Large Blue Become Extinct in Britain? *Oryx*, **15**: 243-247.

Thomas, J.A. 1987. Bringing back the Large Blue. *NERC News*, No. 3: 38-39.

Thomas, J.A. 1989. The History, Decline and Re-establishment of the Large Blue in Devon. *Nature in Devon*, No. 10: 34-44.

Thomas, J.A. & Webb, N. 1984. *Butterflies of Dorset*. Dorchester: Dorset Nat. Hist. & Archaeol. Soc.

Thornett, R. 1988. Diary of a Clouded Yellow Year. *British Butt. Cons. Soc. (Devon Branch) Newsletter*, No. 6: 1-2.

Tolman, T.W.C. 1979. The Brown Hairstreak: *Thecla betulae* L. 1: Searching for Ova. *Ent. Rec. & J. Var.*, **91**: 33-36.

Tuke, S. 1932. *Acherontia atropos* and *Sphinx convolvuli* in East Devon. *Entomologist*, **63**: 262.

Turner, H.J. 1901. Desultory Days at Dawlish. *Proc. S. Lond. Ent. & Nat. Hist. Soc.*, 1900, pp. 21-30.

Turner, M.A. 1964. 16th Annual Report of the Entomological Section. *Rep. & Trans. Devonshire Ass.*, **96**: 45.

Turner, M.A. 1965. 17th Annual Report of the Entomological Section. *Rep. & Trans. Devonshire Ass.*, **97**: 43-49.

Turner, M.A. 1966. 18th Annual Report of the Entomological Section. *Rep. & Trans. Devonshire Ass.*, **98**: 51-59.

Turner, M.A. 1973. 25th Annual Report of the Entomological Section. *Rep. & Trans. Devonshire Ass.*, **105**: 197-200.

Turner, M.A. 1977. 29th Annual Report of the Entomological Section. *Rep. & Trans. Devonshire Ass.*, **109**: 207.

Turner, M.A. 1978. 30th Annual Report of the Entomological Section. *Rep. & Trans. Devonshire Ass.*, **110**: 210.

Turner, M.A. 1979. 31st Annual Report of the Entomological Section. *Rep. & Trans. Devonshire Ass.*, **111**: 183.

Turton, W. and Kingston, J.E. [1830]. *The Natural History of the district of Teignmouth, Dawlish and Torquay*. Teignmouth: E. Croydon.

Tutt, J.W. 1895. Notes on Collecting, Etc. *Ent. Rec. & J. Var.*, **7**: 13-17.

Tutt, J.W. 1907-1908. *A natural history of British Butterflies*, Vol. ix. London: Swan Sonnenschein.

Tyson, K.C. 1987a. In search of Devonian Chalkhill Blues. *British Butt. Cons. Soc. (Devon Branch) Newsletter*, No. 5: 4-5.

Tyson, K.C. 1987b. Clouded Yellows at North Wyke during September 1987. *British Butt. Cons. Soc. (Devon Branch) Newsletter*, No. 5: 6.

Walker, J. 1930. Notes on the Local Lepidoptera. *Trans. & Proc. Torquay Nat. Hist. Soc.*, **5**: 265-275.

Walker, J. 1933. Attempts at Transplantation of Lepidoptera. *Trans. & Proc. Torquay Nat. Hist. Soc.*, **6**: 231-234.

Wallace, T.J. 1967. *The Axmouth - Lyme Regis undercliffs National Nature Reserve*. Annotated lists of insect fauna. Lepidoptera. Section 1, butterflies...rhopalocera. Privately circulated.

Wallace, T.J. 1979. *Some Uncommon Butterfly Species of East Devon*. Privately circulated.

Wallis, W.J. 1944. Rare Butterflies? *Western Morning News*, Aug. 20th?.

Warren, M.S. 1984. The future of the Heath Fritillary in Britain. *Butterfly News (BBCS)*, No. 32: 19-30.

Warren, M.S. 1985. *The ecology and conservation of the heath fritillary butterfly, Mellicta athalia*. Confidential Report to the Nature Conservancy Council (unpublished).

Warren, M.S. 1991. The successful conservation of an endangered species, The Heath Fritillary butterfly *Mellicta athalia*, in Britain. *Biological Conservation*, **52**, 39-56.

Warren, M.S., Thomas, C.D. and Thomas, J.A. 1984. The Status of the Heath Fritillary Butterfly *Mellicta athalia* Rott. in Britain. *Biological Conservation*, **29**: 287-305.

Watkins, N. 1938. Abnormal First Appearance Dates. *Entomologist*, **71**: 161-162.

Wells, H.O. 1897. Collecting at Sidmouth, South Devon. *Entomologist*, **30**: 222-223.

Wells, H.O. 1898. Collecting in South Devon. *Entomologist*, **31**: 245-246.

Whitley, E. 1919. *Eugonia polychloros* in Devon. *Entomologist*, **52**: 216.

Whittle, F.G. 1909. Notes from Sidmouth. *Entomologist*, **42**: 260.

Wild, E.H. 1945. *Pontia daplidice* in N. Devon. *Entomologist*, **78**: 142-143.

Wilkinson, F. 1870. Entomological Notes, Captures, &c. 1870. Abundance of *Leucophasia Sinapis* at Ipplepen, South Devon. *Entomologist*, **5**: 114.

Wood, J.O.N. 1936. *Danaus plexippus* in S. Devon. *Entomologist*, **69**: 230.

Woollatt, L.H. 1943. *Limenitis camilla* L. (Lep. Nymphalidae) in Devonshire. *Entomologist's Monthly Magazine*, **79**: 138.

de Worms, C.G.M. 1962. British Lepidoptera Collecting during 1961. *Entomologist*, **95**: 113-117.

Wright, F.R.E. 1932. *Braunton. A Few Nature Notes*. Barnstaple: Barnes.